EVERY POEM TELLS A STORY

Other anthologies by Raymond Wilson
published by Viking Kestrel

Nine O'Clock Bell
Poems about School

Out and About
Poems of the Outdoors

EVERY POEM TELLS A STORY

Chosen by Raymond Wilson

Illustrated by Alison Darke

VIKING KESTREL

VIKING KESTREL

Published by the Penguin Group
27 Wrights Lane, London W8 5TZ, England
Viking Penguin Inc., 40 West 23rd Street, New York, New York 10010, USA
Penguin Books Australia Ltd, Ringwood, Victoria, Australia
Penguin Books Canada Ltd, 2801 John Street, Markham, Ontario, Canada L3R 1B4
Penguin Books (NZ) Ltd, 182–190 Wairau Road, Auckland 10, New Zealand

Penguin Books Ltd, Registered Offices: Harmondsworth, Middlesex, England

First published 1988
10 9 8 7 6 5 4 3 2 1

Printed in Great Britain by
Butler & Tanner Ltd, Frome & London
Typeset in 11/13pt Lasercomp Baskerville

British Library Cataloguing in Publication Data

Wilson, Raymond, *1925–*
    Every poem tells a story.
    I. Title
    821'.914

    ISBN 0–670–82086–5

Contents

A Poison Tree

I was angry with my friend:
I told my wrath, my wrath did end.
I was angry with my foe:
I told it not, my wrath did grow

And I watered it in fears,
Night and morning with my tears;
And I sunnèd it with smiles,
And with soft deceitful wiles.

And it grew both day and night,
Till it bore an apple bright;
And my foe beheld it shine,
And he knew that it was mine,

And into my garden stole
When the night had veiled the pole:
In the morning glad I see
My foe outstretched beneath the tree.

William Blake

Prince Kano

In a dark wood Prince Kano lost his way
And searched in vain through the long summer's day.
At last, when night was near, he came in sight
Of a small clearing filled with yellow light,
And there, bending beside his brazier, stood
A charcoal burner wearing a black hood.
The Prince cried out for joy: 'Good friend, I'll give
What you will ask: guide me to where I live.'
The man pulled back his hood: he had no face –
Where it should be there was an empty space.

Half dead with fear the Prince staggered away,
Rushed blindly through the wood till break of day;
And then he saw a larger clearing, filled
With houses, people; but his soul was chilled.
He looked around for comfort, and his search
Led him inside a small, half-empty church
Where monks prayed. 'Father,' to one he said,
'I've seen a dreadful thing; I am afraid.'
'What did you see, my son?' 'I saw a man
Whose face was like ...' and, as the Prince began,
The monk drew back his hood and seemed to hiss,
Pointing to where his face should be, 'Like this?'

Edward Lowbury

Hide and Seek

Call out. Call loud; 'I'm ready! Come and find me!'
The sacks in the toolshed smell like the seaside.
They'll never find you in this salty dark,
But be careful that your feet aren't sticking out.
Wiser not to risk another shout.
The floor is cold. They'll probably be searching
The bushes near the swing. Whatever happens
You mustn't sneeze when they come prowling in.
And here they are, whispering at the door;
You've never heard them sound so hushed before.
Don't breathe. Don't move. Stay dumb. Hide in your
    blindness.
They're moving closer, someone stumbles, mutters;
Their words and laughter scuffle, and they're gone.
But don't come out just yet; they'll try the lane
And then the greenhouse and back here again.
They must be thinking that you're very clever,
Getting more puzzled as they search all over.
It seems a long time since they went away.
Your legs are stiff, the cold bites through your coat;
The dark damp smell of sand moves in your throat.
It's time to let them know that you're the winner.
Push off the sacks. Uncurl and stretch. That's better!
Out of the shed and call to them; 'I've won.
Here I am! Come and own up I've caught you!'
The darkening garden watches. Nothing stirs.
The bushes hold their breath; the sun is gone.
Yes, here you are. But where are they who sought you?

Vernon Scannell

Storytime

Once upon a time, children,
there lived a fearsome dragon ...

Please miss,
Jamie's made a dragon.
Out in the sandpit.

Lovely, Andrew.
Now this dragon
had enormous red eyes
and a swirling, whirling tail ...

Jamie's dragon's got
yellow eyes, miss.

Lovely, Andrew.
Now this dragon was
as wide as a horse
as green as the grass
as tall as a house ...

Jamie's would JUST fit
in our classroom, miss!

But he was a very friendly dragon ...

Jamie's dragon ISN'T, miss.
He eats people, miss.
Especially TEACHERS,
Jamie said.

Very nice, Andrew!
Now one day, children,
this enormous dragon
rolled his red eye,
whirled his swirly green tail
and set off to find ...

His dinner, miss!
Because he was hungry, miss!

Thank you, Andrew.
He rolled his red eye,
whirled his green tail,
and opened his wide, wide mouth
until o

o o o o o u u a a a h !

Please miss,
I did try to tell you, miss!

Judith Nicholls

Lady Weeping

Lady, weeping at the crossroads
Would you meet your love
In the twilight with his greyhounds
And the hawk on his glove?

Bribe the birds then on the branches,
Bribe them to be dumb,
Stare the hot sun out of heaven
That the night may come.

Starless are the nights of travel,
Bleak the winter wind;
Run with terror all before you
And regret behind.

Run until you hear the ocean's
Everlasting cry;
Deep though it may be and bitter
You must drink it dry.

Wear out patience in the lowest
Dungeons of the sea,
Searching through the stranded shipwrecks
For the golden key.

Push on to the world's end, pay the
Dread guard with a kiss;
Cross the rotten bridge that totters
Over the abyss.

There stands the deserted castle
Ready to explore;
Enter, climb the marble staircase
Open the locked door.

Cross the silent empty ballroom,
Doubt and danger past;
Blow the cobwebs from the mirror
See yourself at last.

Put your hand behind the wainscot,
You have done your part;
Find the penknife there and plunge it
Into your false heart.

W. H. Auden

The Visitor

A crumbling churchyard, the sea and the moon;
The waves had gouged out grave and bone;
A man was walking, late and alone ...

He saw a skeleton on the ground;
A ring on a bony finger he found.

He ran home to his wife and gave her the ring.
'Oh, where did you get it?' He said not a thing.

'It's the loveliest ring in the world,' she said,
As it glowed on her finger. They slipped off to bed.

At midnight they woke. In the dark outside,
'Give me my ring!' a chill voice cried.

'What was that, William? What did it say?'
'Don't worry, my dear. It'll soon go away.'

'I'm coming!' A skeleton opened the door.
'Give me my ring!' It was crossing the floor.

'What was that, William? What did it say?'
'Don't worry, my dear. It'll soon go away.'

'I'm reaching you now! I'm climbing the bed.'
The wife pulled the sheet right over her head.

It was torn from her grasp and tossed in the air:
'I'll drag you out of bed by the hair!'

'What was that, William? What did it say?'
'Throw the ring through the window! THROW IT
  AWAY!'

She threw it. The skeleton leapt from the sill,
Scooped up the ring and clattered downhill,
Fainter ... and fainter ... Then all was still.

Ian Serraillier

The Horse That Had a Flat Tire

Once upon a valley
there came down
from some goldenblue mountains
a handsome young prince
who was riding
a dawncolored horse
named Lordsburg.

> I love you
> You're my breathing castle
> Gentle so gentle
> We'll live forever

In the valley
there was a beautiful maiden
whom the prince
drifted into love with
like a New Mexico made from
apple thunder and long
glass beads.

> I love you
> You're my breathing castle
> Gentle so gentle
> We'll live forever

The prince enchanted
the maiden
and they rode off
on the dawncolored horse
named Lordsburg
toward the goldenblue mountains.

I love you
You're my breathing castle
Gentle so gentle
We'll live forever

They would have lived
happily ever after
if the horse hadn't had
a flat tire
in front of a dragon's
house.

Richard Brautigan

As Mary was A-walking

As Mary was a-walking
   By Bethlehem one day,
Her Son was in her arms,
   So heavenly to see.

'O give me water, Mother.'
   'You cannot drink, my dear;
For the rivers they are muddy,
   And the streams they are not clear;

'The rivers they are muddy,
   And the streams they are not clear,
And the springs are full of blood,
   You cannot drink from here.'

They came into a grove,
   So thick with oranges
That not another orange
   Could hang upon the trees;
There sat a man to guard them,
   Was blind in both his eyes.

'Give me an orange, blind man,
   To feed my Son today.'
'And take as many, lady,
   As you can bear away;

'Gather the biggest, lady,
   That most are to your mind,
The small ones soon will ripen,
   If you leave them behind.'

They gathered them by one and one,
    There grew a hundred more,
And straight the man began to see
    That had been blind before.

'O who is this fair lady,
    Has made me see again?'
It was the Holy Virgin
    That walked by Bethlehem.

Unknown
translated from the Spanish by
Edith C. Batho

Conquerors

By sundown we came to a hidden village
Where all the air was still
And no sound met our tired ears, save
For the sorry drip of rain from blackened trees
And the melancholy song of swinging gates.
Then through a broken pane some of us saw
A dead bird in a rusting cage, still
Pressing his thin tattered breast against the bars,
His beak wide open. And
As we hurried through the weed-grown street,
A gaunt dog started up from some dark place
And shambled off on legs as thin as sticks
Into the wood, to die at least in peace.
No one had told us victory was like this;
Not one amongst us would have eaten bread
Before he'd filled the mouth of the grey child
That sprawled, stiff as stone, before the shattered door.
There was not one who did not think of home.

Henry Treece

The Fugitive

That ditch of rushes, is it deep
Enough for me to creep
And hide there, till the pursuing horsemen pass?
The osier, will it droop
And cloak me, while the troop
Thuds o'er the miry track among the grass?

My scarf of crimson I have thrown
Into a puddle brown;
They will catch no glint of red beneath the trees;
I may escape their eyes,
But these wild breaths that rise
And buffet me, hearkening they might hear these!

Spur rascals, that your clattering din
May drown all else therein,
That I may gasp and sob unheard of you!
Spur – for if ye draw rein
I shall not see again
The meadows pranked with pearls of morning dew.

The dew of dusk will glimmer soon
And the derisive moon
Look down – on what? – They pass! Their thundering rush
Knocks louder on my ear;
Nay, 'tis my heart I hear –
They have drawn rein to listen. One said '*Hush!*'

Dorothy Stuart

As I Walked Out in the Streets of Laredo

As I walked out in the streets of Laredo,
As I walked out in Laredo one day,
I spied a poor cowboy wrapped up in white linen,
Wrapped up in white linen as cold as the clay.

'I see by your outfit that you are a cowboy,'
These words he did say as I boldly stepped by.
'Come, sit down beside me and hear my sad story;
I was shot in the breast and I know I must die.

Once in my saddle I used to look handsome,
Once in my saddle I used to look gay.
I first went to drinkin' and then to card playin',
Got shot in the breast, which ended my day.

Let sixteen gamblers come handle my coffin,
Let sixteen girls come carry my pall;
Put bunches of roses all over my coffin,
Put roses to deaden the clods as they fall.

And beat the drums slowly and play the fife lowly,
And play the dead march as you carry me along;
Take me to the prairie and lay the sod o'er me,
For I'm a young cowboy and I know I've done wrong.'

We beat the drums slowly and played the fife lowly,
And bitterly wept as we bore him along;
For we all loved our comrade so brave, young and
   handsome,
We loved the young cowboy although he'd done wrong.

                              Unknown

A Phantasy

This plump boy, simple, scared of everything
Told me he'd like to live in a cardboard box
With eye holes, ear holes, air holes.

After two years of treatment he had reached the point
Where only one fear remained: drowning.
He had nightmares of being sucked into the waves.

A hundred miles from the sea, walking
To school along a road two miles from any water,
A grain truck passed him on a tight corner,

Spilled its load over him.
The driver said he saw the grain moving
And tried, though injured, to dig down.

There were sounds too. Long bleating cries.   .
He thought it was a sheep he'd buried.
And the boy died.

John Ashbrook

A Chinese Poem Written in 718 BC

The K'e still ripples to its banks,
   The moorfowl cry.
My hair was gathered in a knot,
   And you came by.
Selling of silk you were, a lad
   Not of our kin;
You passed at sunset on the road
   From far-off Ts'in.
The frogs were croaking in the dusk;
   The grass was wet.
We talked together, and I laughed;
   I hear it yet.
I thought that I would be your wife;
   I had your word.
And so I took the road with you,
   And crossed the ford.
I do not know when first it was
   Your eyes looked cold.
But all this was three years ago
   And I am old.

Unknown
translated from the Chinese by
Arthur Waley

Brennan on the Moor

It's of a fearless highwayman a story I will tell,
His name was Willie Brennan and in Ireland he did dwell.
'Twas on the Kilworth mountains he began a wild career,
And many a noble gentleman before him shook with fear.

Crying Brennan's on the moor! Brennan's on the moor!
So bold and undaunted stood Bill Brennan on the moor.

'Twas on the King's own highway now Brennan he sat
    down,
He met the Mayor of Cashel just five miles out of town.
The Mayor he looked at Brennan and, 'I think now, boy,'
    says he,
'Your name is Billie Brennan; you must come along with
    me.'

Now Brennan's wife was going down town provisions for to
    buy,
And she seen Willie taken, ah sure she began to cry,
'Hand me ten pennies!' and sure just as he spoke,
She handed him a blunderbuss from underneath her cloak.

Brennan had his blunderbuss, my story I'll unfold,
He caused the Mayor of Cashel to deliver up his gold.
Five thousand pounds were offered for his apprehension
    there,
But Brennan and the pedlar to the mountain did repair.

Now Brennan is an outlaw upon a mountain high,
With Infantry and Cavalry to catch him they did try,
He laughed at them, he scorned at them until, it is said,
A false-hearted woman caused him to lose his head.

They hung him at the crossroads, in chains he swung and
    dried,
Some say in the midnight hour you still can see him ride.
You'll see him with his blunderbuss, and in the midnight
    chill
Along the King's own highway rides Willie Brennan still.

Unknown

The Explosion

On the day of the explosion
Shadows pointed towards the pithead:
In the sun the slagheap slept.

Down the lane came men in pitboots
Coughing oath-edged talk and pipe-smoke,
Shouldering off the freshened silence.

One chased after rabbits; lost them;
Came back with a nest of lark's eggs;
Showed them; lodged them in the grasses.

So they passed in beards and moleskins,
Fathers, brothers, nicknames, laughter,
Through the tall gates standing open.

At noon, there came a tremor; cows
Stopped chewing for a second; sun,
Scarfed as in a heat-haze, dimmed.

The dead go on before us, they
Are sitting in God's house in comfort,
We shall see them face to face –

Plain as lettering in the chapels
It was said, and for a second
Wives saw men of the explosion

Larger than in life they managed –
Gold as on a coin, or walking
Somehow from the sun towards them,

One showing the eggs unbroken.

Philip Larkin

The Man on the Flying Trapeze

Oh the girl that I loved she was handsome,
I tried all I knew her to please,
But I couldn't please her a quarter as well
As the man on the flying trapeze.

Oh, he flies through the air with the greatest of ease,
That daring young man on the flying trapeze.
His figure is handsome, all girls he can please,
And my love he purloined her away.

Last night as usual I went to her home.
There sat her old father and mother alone.
I asked for my love and they soon made it known
That she–e had flown away.

She packed up her box and eloped in the night,
To go–o with him at his ease.
He lowered her down from a four-storey flight,
By means of his flying trapeze.

He took her to town and he dressed her in tights,
That he might live at his ease.
He ordered her up to the tent's awful height,
To appear on the flying trapeze.

Now she flies through the air with the greatest of ease,
This daring young girl on the flying trapeze.
Her figure is handsome, all men she can please,
And my love is purloined away.

Once I was happy, but now I'm forlorn,
Like an old coat that is tattered and torn,
Left to this wide world to fret and to mourn,
Betrayed by a maid in her teens.

Unknown

Sheep

When I was once in Baltimore
A man came up to me and cried,
'Come, I have eighteen hundred sheep,
And we will sail on Tuesday's tide.

'If you will sail with me, young man,
I'll pay you fifty shillings down;
These eighteen hundred sheep I take
From Baltimore to Glasgow town.'

He paid me fifty shillings down.
I sailed with eighteen hundred sheep;
We soon had cleared the harbour's mouth,
We soon were in the salt sea deep.

The first night we were out at sea
Those sheep were quiet in their mind;
The second night they cried with fear –
They smelt no pastures in the wind.

They sniffed, poor things, for their green fields.
They cried so loud I could not sleep:
For fifty thousand shillings down
I would not sail again with sheep.

W. H. Davies

The Ass' Song

In a nearby town
There lived an Ass,

Who in his life –
As all good Asses do –

Served his Master
Faithfully and true.

When this Ass died
And fled above,

For his reward –
That all good Asses have –

The Master made
From his loyal hide

A whip with which
His successor was lashed.

In a nearby town
His successor is lashed.

Christopher Logue

Applemoon

Something woke me: startle-sound
or moonlight. The house dreamt
like an old cat, but I
looked out my window.

And night was day in a midnight
moon-flood. Mazy moon
flaring a halo of quick clouds
running the big black sky.
And I saw a thousand windfall apples
lying luminous as sea-stones beached
below the spiky silver trees.

So, shivering I
mouse-went out
with a basket, barefoot, toes
curling in the cold;
and singing soft
took ripe reluctant apples
under close and curious stars.

Only soon I saw
my shadow was not
the same as I;
it stooped more –
had its own thinness . . .
and our fingers
never met.

I quick-ran back
the house so
sleepy-warm, sure.
But looking out through curtain lace
I saw my shadow linger
moving slow and crooked, plucking
shadow apples
from the shining moony grass.

Rose Flint

The Tide Rises, the Tide Falls

The tide rises, the tide falls,
The twilight darkens, the curlew calls;
Along the sea-sands damp and brown
The traveller hastens toward the town,
    And the tide rises, the tide falls.

Darkness settles on roofs and walls,
But the sea, the sea in the darkness calls;
The little waves, with their soft, white hands,
Efface the footprints in the sands,
    And the tide rises, the tide falls.

The morning breaks; the steeds in their stalls
Stamp and neigh, as the hostler calls;
The day returns, but nevermore
Returns the traveller to the shore,
    And the tide rises, the tide falls.

Henry Wadsworth Longfellow

Lady Diamond

There was a king, and a glorious king,
    A king of noble fame,
And he had daughters only one,
    Lady Diamond was her name.

He had a boy, a kitchen boy,
    A boy of muckle scorn,
She loved him long, she loved him aye,
    Till the grass o'er grew the corn.

When twenty weeks were gone and past,
    O she began to greet,
For her petticoats grew short before,
    And her stays they wouldn't meet.

It fell upon one winter's night,
    The king could get no rest,
He came unto his daughter dear,
    Just like a wandering ghost.

He came unto her bed chamber,
    Pulled back the curtains long,
'What aileth thee my daughter dear,
    I fear you have gotten wrong.'

'O if I have, despise me not,
    For he is all my joy,
I will forsake both dukes and earls
    And marry your kitchen boy.'

'O bring to me my merry men all,
　　By thirty and by three,
O bring to me my kitchen boy,
　　We'll murder him secretly.'

There was not a sound into the hall,
　　And ne'er a word was said,
Until they got him safe and sure,
　　Between two feather beds.

'Cut the heart from out of his breast,
　　Put it in a cup of gold,
And present it to his Diamond dear,
　　For she was both stout and bold.'

'O come to me, my hinnie, my heart,
　　O come to me my joy,
O come to me, my hinnie, my heart,
　　My father's kitchen boy.'

She took the cup from out of their hands,
  And she set it at her bed head.
She washed it with tears that fell from her eyes,
  And next morning she was dead.

'O where were you my merry men all,
  That I gave meat and wage,
That you didn't stay my cruel hand,
  When I was in a rage?

For gone is all my heart's delight,
  O gone is all my joy,
For my dear Diamond she is dead,
  Likewise my kitchen boy.'

Unknown

of muckle scorn greatly despised
greet weep
hinnie honey

Never since Eden

The Thing that came from Outer Space
And landed in the Jones' backyard
Had neither colour, size nor shape,
But a smell that caught us all off guard.

Never since Eden had there been
So sweet, so rich, so good a smell:
The neighbours, sniffing, gathered round
Like thirsting cattle at a well.

Never since Adam first kissed Eve
Had humans looked upon each other
With such joy that old enemies
Threw loving arms round one another.

One whiff, and babies stopped their crying,
And all the gossip was kind and good,
And thieves and thugs and hooligans
Danced in the street in holiday mood.

Old scores were settled with a smile,
And liars changed to honest men,
And the ugliest face was beautiful,
And the sick and infirm were made whole again.

The Thing that came from Outer Space
Purred like a cat at the heart of the smell,
But *how* it did, and *why* it did,
Was more than the Scientists could tell.

They roped it off, they cleared the streets,
They closed upon it, wearing masks,
Ringed it with Geiger counters, scooped
And sealed it in aseptic flasks.

They took it back to analyse
In laboratories white and bare,
And they proved with burette and chromatograph
That nothing whatever was there.

They sterilized the Jones' backyard
(The smell whimpered and died without trace),
Then they showed by mathematics that no Thing
Could have landed from Outer Space.

So the neighbours are quite their old selves now,
As loving as vipers or stoats,
Cheating and lying and waiting their chance
To leap at each other's throats.

Raymond Wilson

The Unquiet Grave

'The wind doth blow today, my love,
And a few small drops of rain;
I never had but one true-love;
In cold grave she was lain.

'I'll do as much for my true-love
As any young man may;
I'll sit and mourn upon her grave
A twelvemonth and a day.'

The twelvemonth and a day being up,
The dead began to speak;
'Oh who sits weeping on my grave,
And will not let me sleep?'

"'Tis I, my only love, sit on your grave,
And will not let you sleep;
For I crave one kiss of your clay-cold lips,
And that is all I seek.'

'You crave one kiss of my clay-cold lips
But my breath smells earthly strong,
If you have one kiss of my clay-cold lips,
Your time will not be long.

'Down in yonder garden gay,
Love, where we used to walk,
The sweetest flower that ever I saw
Is withered to a stalk.

'The stalk is withered dry, my love,
So will our hearts decay;
So make yourself content, my love,
Till God calls you away.'

                    Unknown

Jimmy Jet and His TV Set

I'll tell you the story of Jimmy Jet –
And you know what I tell you is true.
He loved to watch his TV set
Almost as much as you.

He watched all day, he watched all night
Till he grew pale and lean,
From *The Early Show* to *The Late Late Show*
And all the shows between.

He watched till his eyes were frozen wide,
And his bottom grew into his chair.
And his chin turned into a tuning dial,
And antennae grew out of his hair.

And his brains turned into TV tubes,
And his face to a TV screen.
And two knobs saying 'VERT.' and 'HORIZ.'
Grew where his ears had been.

And he grew a plug that looked like a tail
So we plugged in little Jim.
And now instead of him watching TV
We all sit around and watch him.

Shel Silverstein

Fairy Tale

He made himself a house,
   his foundations,
   his stones,
   his walls,
   his roof overhead,
   his chimney and smoke,
   his view from the window.

He made himself a garden,
   his fence,
   his thyme,
   his earthworm,
   his evening dew.

He cut out his bit of sky above.

And he wrapped the garden in the sky
and the house in the garden
and packed the lot in a handkerchief

and went off
lone as an arctic fox
through the cold
unending
rain
into the world.

                  Miroslav Holub

The Charge of the Light Brigade

Half a league, half a league,
Half a league onward,
All in the valley of Death
Rode the six hundred.
'Forward the Light Brigade!
Charge for the guns,' he said:
Into the valley of Death
Rode the six hundred.

'Forward, the Light Brigade!'
Was there a man dismayed?
Not though the soldier knew
Someone had blundered:
Theirs not to make reply,
Theirs not to reason why,
Theirs but to do and die:
Into the valley of Death
Rode the six hundred.

Cannon to right of them,
Cannon to left of them,
Cannon in front of them
Volleyed and thundered;
Stormed at with shot and shell,
Boldly they rode and well,
Into the jaws of Death,
Into the mouth of Hell
Rode the six hundred.

Flashed all their sabres bare,
Flashed as they turned in air
Sabring the gunners there,
Charging an army, while
All the world wondered.
Plunged in the battery-smoke
Right through the line they broke,
Cossack and Russian
Reeled from the sabre-stroke
Shattered and sundered.
Then they rode back, but not
Not the six hundred.

Cannon to right of them,
Cannon to left of them,
Cannon in front of them
Volleyed and thundered;
Stormed at with shot and shell,
While horse and hero fell,
They that had fought so well
Came through the jaws of Death,
Back from the mouth of Hell,
All that was left of them,
Left of six hundred.

When can their glory fade?
O the wild charge they made!
All the world wondered.
Honour the charge they made!
Honour the Light Brigade,
Noble six hundred!

Alfred, Lord Tennyson

The Song of Wandering Aengus

I went out to the hazel wood,
Because a fire was in my head,
And cut and peeled a hazel wand,
And hooked a berry to a thread;
And when white moths were on the wing,
And moth-like stars were flickering out,
I dropped the berry in a stream
And caught a little silver trout.

When I had laid it on the floor
I went to blow the fire aflame,
But something rustled on the floor,
And some one called me by my name:
It had become a glimmering girl
With apple blossom in her hair
Who called me by my name and ran
And faded through the brightening air.

Though I am old with wandering
Through hollow lands and hilly lands,
I will find out where she has gone,
And kiss her lips and take her hands;
And walk among long dappled grass,
And pluck till time and times are done
The silver apples of the moon,
The golden apples of the sun.

W. B. Yeats

The Wife of Usher's Well

There lived a wife at Usher's Well,
  And a wealthy wife was she;
She had three stout and stalwart sons,
  And sent them o'er the sea.

They hadna been a week frae her,
  A week but barely ane,
When word cam to the carline wife
  That her three sons were gane.

They hadna been a week frae her,
  A week but barely three,
When word cam to the carline wife
  That her sons she'd never see.

'I wish the wind may never cease,
  Nor fashes in the flood,
Till my three sons come hame to me
  In earthly flesh and blood!'

It fell about the Martinmas,
  When nights are lang and mirk,
The carline wife's three sons cam hame,
  And their hats were o'the birk.

It neither grew in syke nor ditch,
  Nor yet in ony sheugh;
But at the gates o' Paradise
  That birk grew fair eneugh.

'Blow up the fire, my maidens!
   Bring water frae the well!
For a' my house shall feast this night,
   Since my three sons are well.'

And she has made to them a bed,
   She's made it large and wide;
And she's ta'en her mantle her about,
   Sat down at the bedside.

Up then crew the red, red cock,
   And up and crew the grey;
The eldest to the youngest said,
   ''Tis time we were away.'

The cock he hadna crawed but once,
   And clapped his wings at a',
When the youngest to the eldest said,
   'Brother, we maun awa'.'

'The cock doth craw, the day doth daw',
   The channerin' worm doth chide;
'Gin we be missed out o' our place,
   · A sair pain we maun bide.'

'Lie still, lie still but a little wee while,
   Lie still but if we may;
'Gin my mother should miss us when she wakes,
   She'll go mad ere it be day.'

'Fare ye weel, my mother dear!
   Fare weel to barn and byre.
And fare ye weel, the bonny lass
   That kindles my mother's fire!'

Unknown

carline old
syke stream
sheugh trench

Danny Deever

'What are the bugles blowin' for?' said Files-on-Parade.
'To turn you out, to turn you out,' the Colour-Sergeant
said.
'What makes you look so white, so white?' said Files-on-
Parade.
'I'm dreadin' what I've got to watch,' the Colour-Sergeant
said.
> For they're hangin' Danny Deever, you can hear the
> Dead March play,
> The Regiment's in 'ollow square – they're hangin' him
> today;
> They've taken of his buttons off an' cut his stripes away
> An' they're hangin' Danny Deever in the mornin'.

'What makes the rear-rank breathe so 'ard?' said Files-on-
Parade.
'It's bitter cold, it's bitter cold,' the Colour-Sergeant said.
'What makes that front-rank man fall down?' said Files-on-
Parade.
'A touch o' sun, a touch o' sun,' the Colour-Sergeant said.
> They are hangin' Danny Deever, they are marchin' of
> 'im round,
> They 'ave 'alted Danny Deever by 'is coffin on the
> ground;
> An' 'e'll swing in 'arf a minute for a sneakin' shootin'
> hound –
> O they're hangin' Danny Deever in the mornin'!

''Is cot was right-'and cot to mine,' said Files-on-Parade.
''E's sleepin' out an' far tonight,' the Colour-Sergeant said.
'I've drunk 'is beer a score o' times,' said Files-on-Parade.
''E's drinkin' bitter beer alone,' the Colour-Sergeant said.
> They are hangin' Danny Deever, you must mark 'im
> to 'is place,
> For 'e shot a comrade sleepin' – you must look 'im in
> the face;
> Nine 'undred of 'is county an' the Regiment's disgrace,
> While they're hangin' Danny Deever in the mornin'.

'What's that so black agin the sun?' said Files-on-Parade.
'It's Danny fightin' 'ard for life,' the Colour-Sergeant said.
'What's that that whimpers over'ead?' said Files-on-Parade.
'It's Danny's soul that's passin' now,' the Colour-Sergeant
said.
> For they're done with Danny Deever, you can 'ear the
> quickstep play,
> The Regiment's in column, an' they're marchin' us
> away;
> Ho! the young recruits are shakin', an' they'll want
> their beer today,
> After hangin' Danny Deever in the mornin'!

Rudyard Kipling

Abou Ben Adhem

Abou Ben Adhem (may his tribe increase)
Awoke one night from a deep dream of peace,
And saw within the moonlight in his room
Making it rich, and like a lily in bloom,
An angel writing in a book of gold:
Exceeding peace had made Ben Adhem bold,
And to the presence in the room he said,
'What writest thou?' – The vision raised its head,
And with a look made of all sweet accord,
Answered, 'The names of those who love the Lord.'
'And is mine one?' said Abou. 'Nay, not so,'
Replied the angel. Abou spoke more low,
But cheerily still and said, 'I pray thee then,
Write me as one that loves his fellow men.'

The angel wrote, and vanished. The next night
It came again with a great wakening light,
And showed the names whom love of God has blessed,
And lo! Ben Adhem's name led all the rest.

Leigh Hunt

A Fable

A crazy hunter, following a bear,
And pressing harder than a man should dare,
Was menaced by a leopard and a lion.
Availed no prayer, no cries to Heaven or Zion,
For he had slain their cubs, and with vile blows,
And welded Sky to Jungle by their woes.

Gazing upon a tree, he swiftly fled.
But in his path the bear with turning tread
Firm hindered the supposed security.
Oh, what to do? How save himself from three?
Dropping his gun, he howled and beat the air;
Then, stretching wide his arms, embraced the bear.
'Save me, sweet beast!' he cried. 'Love! Lick my face!'
Which the bear did, returning the embrace.

You know the rest, you know that tightening squeeze.
Only to think, it makes your spirit freeze;
Only to think, it pulls you to the ground,
And makes your blood run cold, your head go round.

Moral: To wicked beasts be straight and fair;
But do not pet them. Face them, and beware!
And never drop your gun to hug a bear.

Herbert Palmer

Lord Ullin's Daughter

A chieftain, to the Highlands bound,
  Cries, 'Boatman, do not tarry,
And I'll give thee a silver pound
  To row us o'er the ferry.'

'Now who be ye would cross Lochgyle,
  This dark and stormy water?'
'O, I'm the chief of Ulva's isle,
  And this Lord Ullin's daughter.

'And fast before her father's men
  Three days we've fled together,
For should he find us in the glen,
  My blood would stain the heather.

'His horsemen hard behind us ride;
    Should they our steps discover,
Then who will cheer my bonny bride
    When they have slain her lover?'

Out spoke the hardy Highland wight,
    'I'll go, my chief, I'm ready!
It is not for your silver bright;
    But for your winsome lady.

'And by my word! the bonny bird
    In danger shall not tarry;
So though the waves are raging white,
    I'll row you o'er the ferry.'

By this the storm grew loud apace,
    The water-wraith was shrieking,
And in the scowl of Heaven each face
    Grew dark as they were speaking.

But still as wilder blew the wind,
    And as the night grew drearer,
Adown the glen rode armèd men,
    Their trampling sounded nearer.

'O haste thee, haste!' the lady cries,
    'Though tempests round us gather;
I'll meet the raging of the skies,
    But not an angry father.'

The boat has left a stormy land,
    A stormy sea before her –
When, oh! too strong, for human hand,
    The tempest gathered o'er her.

And still they rowed amidst the roar
    Of waters fast prevailing;
Lord Ullin reached that fatal shore,
    His wrath was changed to wailing.

For sore dismayed, through storm and shade,
    His child he did discover:
One lovely hand she stretched for aid,
    And one was round her lover.

'Come back! come back!' he cried in grief,
    'Across this stormy water;
And I'll forgive your Highland chief,
    My daughter! Oh, my daughter!'

'Twas vain: the loud waves lashed the shore,
    Return or aid preventing;
The waters wild went o'er his child,
    And he was left lamenting.

Thomas Campbell

Lord Randal

'O, where hae ye been, Lord Randal, my son?
O, where hae ye been, my handsome young man?' –
'I have been to the wild wood; mother, make my bed soon,
For I'm weary wi' hunting, and fain wald lie down.'

'Where gat ye your dinner, Lord Randal, my son?
Where gat ye your dinner, my handsome young man?' –
'I dined wi' my true-love; mother, make my bed soon,
For I'm weary wi' hunting, and fain wald lie down.'

'What gat ye to your dinner, Lord Randal, my son?
What gat ye to your dinner, my handsome young man?'
'I gat eels boiled in bro'; mother, make my bed soon,
For I'm weary wi' hunting, and fain wald lie down.'

'What became of your bloodhounds, Lord Randal, my son?
What became of your bloodhounds, my handsome young
    man?' –
'O they swelled and they died; mother, make my bed soon,
For I'm weary wi' hunting, and fain wald lie down.'

'O, I fear ye are poisoned, Lord Randal, my son!
O, I fear ye are poisoned, my handsome young man!' –
'O, yes, I am poisoned; mother, make my bed soon,
For I'm sick at the heart, and I fain wald lie down.'

Unknown

The Huntsman

Kagwa hunted the lion,
   Through bush and forest went his spear.
One day he found the skull of a man
   And said to it, 'How did you come here?'
The skull opened its mouth and said
   'Talking brought me here.'

Kagwa hurried home;
   Went to the king's chair and spoke:
'In the forest I found a talking skull.'
   The king was silent. Then he said slowly,
'Never since I was born of my mother
   Have I seen or heard of a skull which spoke.'

The king called out his guards:
   'Two of you now go with him
And find this talking skull;
   But if his tale is a lie
And the skull speaks no word,
   This Kagwa himself must die.'

They rode into the forest;
   For days and nights they found nothing.
At last they saw the skull; Kagwa
   Said to it 'How did you come here?'
The skull said nothing. Kagwa implored,
   But the skull said nothing.

The guards said, 'Kneel down.'
   They killed him with sword and spear.
Then the skull opened its mouth;
   'Huntsman, how did you come here?'
And the dead man answered,
   'Talking brought me here.'

                Edward Lowbury

Legend

The blacksmith's boy went out with a rifle
and a black dog running behind.
Cobwebs snatched at his feet,
rivers hindered him,
thorn-branches caught at his eyes to make him blind
and the sky turned into an unlucky opal,
but he didn't mind.
I can break branches, I can swim rivers, I can stare out any
   spider I meet,
said he to his dog and his rifle.

The blacksmith's boy went over the paddocks
with his old black hat on his head.
Mountains jumped in his way,
rocks rolled down on him,
and the old crow cried, You'll soon be dead;
and the rain came down like mattocks.
But he only said
I can climb mountains, I can dodge rocks, I can shoot an
   old crow any day.
And he went on over the paddocks.

When he came to the end of the day the sun began falling.
Up came the night ready to swallow him,
like the barrel of a gun,
like an old black hat,
like a black dog hungry to follow him.
Then the pigeon, the magpie and the dove began wailing,
and the grass lay down to pillow him.
His rifle broke, his hat blew away and his dog was gone,
and the sun was falling.

But in front of the night the rainbow stood on the mountain
just as his heart foretold.
He ran like a hare,
he climbed like a fox,
he caught it in his hands, the colours and the cold –
like a bar of ice, like the columns of a fountain,
like a ring of gold.
The pigeon, the magpie and the dove flew up to stare,
and the grass stood up again on the mountain.

The blacksmith's boy hung the rainbow on his shoulder,
instead of his broken gun.
Lizards ran out to see,
snakes made way for him,
and the rainbow shone as brightly as the sun.
All the world said, Nobody is braver, nobody is bolder,
nobody else has done
anything to equal it. He went home as easy as could be
with the swinging rainbow on his shoulder.

Judith Wright

(

The Great Silkie
of Sule Skerrie

In Norway there sits a maid:
'By-loo, my baby,' she begins,
'Little know I my child's father
Or if land or sea he's living in.'

Then there arose at her bed feet,
And a grumly guest I'm sure it was he,
Saying 'Here am I, thy child's father,
Although that I am not comely.

'I am a man upon the land,
I am a silkie in the sea,
And when I am in my own country,
My dwelling is in Sule Skerrie.'

Then he hath taken a purse of gold,
He hath put it upon her knee,
Saying 'Give to me my little wee son,
And take thee up thy nurse's fee.

'And it shall come to pass on a summer day,
When the sun shines hot on every stone,
That I shall take my little wee son,
And I'll teach him for to swim in the foam.

'And you will marry a gunner good
And a proud good gunner I'm sure he'll be.
And he'll go out on a May morning
And he'll kill both my wee son and me.'

And lo, she did marry a gunner good,
And a proud good gunner I'm sure it was he;
And the very first shot that e'er he did shoot
He killed the son and the great silkie.

In Norway there sits a maid:
'By-loo, my baby,' she begins,
'Little know I my child's father
Or if land or sea he's living in.'

Unknown

silkie seal

An Elegy on the Death of a Mad Dog

Good people all, of every sort,
  Give ear unto my song;
And if you find it wondrous short,
  It cannot hold you long.

In Islington there was a man,
  Of whom the world might say,
That still a godly race he ran,
  Whene'er he went to pray.

A kind and gentle heart he had,
  To comfort friends and foes;
The naked every day he clad,
  When he put on his clothes.

And in that town a dog was found,
  As many dogs there be,
Both mongrel, puppy, whelp, and hound,
  And curs of low degree.

This dog and man at first were friends;
  But when a pique began,
The dog, to gain his private ends,
  Went mad, and bit the man.

Around from all the neighbouring streets
  The wondering neighbours ran,
And swore the dog had lost his wits,
  To bite so good a man.

The wound it seemed both sore and sad
    To every Christian eye;
And while they swore the dog was mad,
    They swore the man would die.

But soon a wonder came to light,
    That showed the rogues they lied;
The man recovered of the bite,
    The dog it was that died.

Oliver Goldsmith

The Inquest

I took my oath I would inquire,
   Without affection, hate, or wrath,
Into the death of Ada Wright –
   So help me God! I took that oath.

When I went out to see the corpse,
   The four months' babe that died so young,
I judged it was seven pounds in weight,
   And little more than one foot long.

One eye, that had a yellow lid,
   Was shut – so was the mouth, that smiled;
The left eye open, shining bright –
   It seemed a knowing little child.

For as I looked at that one eye,
   It seemed to laugh, and say with glee:
'What caused my death you'll never know –
   Perhaps my mother murdered me.'

When I went into court again,
    To hear the mother's evidence –
It was a love-child, she explained,
    And smiled, for our intelligence.

'Now, Gentlemen of the Jury,' said
    The coroner – 'this woman's child
By misadventure met its death.'
    'Aye, aye,' said we. The mother smiled

And I could see that child's one eye
    Which seemed to laugh, and say with glee:
'What caused my death you'll never know –
    Perhaps my mother murdered me.'

W. H. Davies

The King and the Clown
A Persian Tale

There was once a monarch, a pompous old Persian,
Whose frown was a threat and his nod a command.
Yet there at his side, as a needed diversion,
A quick-witted jester was always on hand.

For a while there were smiles, for a while there was laughter;
Then, one evil day, the king's petulance spoke:
'There's been too much fooling. You're finished! and after
You're dead, you'll discover that life is no joke.

'I might have you tortured, then add something crueller;
Hung up by your toe-nails or torn by a cur;
But I am a merry and merciful ruler,
And so you may choose any death you prefer.'

The clown paled and wept. Then abrupt, he stopped crying,
And grinned at the monarch. 'Don't fly in a rage,
I choose (and I thank you) to die of old age.'

Michael Lewis

Winter: East Anglia

In a frosty sunset
    So fiery red with cold
The footballers' onset
    Rings out glad and bold;
Then boys from daily tether
    With famous dogs at heel
In starlight meet together
    And to farther hedges steal;
Where the rats are pattering
    In and out the stacks,
Owls with hatred chattering
    Swoop at the terriers' backs.
And, frost forgot, the chase grows hot
    Till a rat's a foolish prize,
But the cornered weasel stands his ground,
Shrieks at the dogs and boys set round,
Shrieks as he knows they stand all round,
    And hard as winter dies.

Edmund Blunden

The Whale

O, 'twas in the year of ninety-four,
And of June the second day,
That our gallant ship her anchor weighed
And from Stromness bore away, brave boys!
  And from Stromness bore away!

Now Speedicut was our captain's name,
And our ship the *Lion* bold,
And we were bound to far Greenland,
To the land of ice and cold – brave boys,
  To the land of ice and cold.

And when we came to far Greenland,
And to Greenland cold came we,
Where there's ice, and there's snow, and the whalefishes
  blow,
We found all open sea – brave boys,
  We found all open sea.

Then the mate he climbed to the crow's nest high,
With his spy-glass in his hand,
'There's a whale, there's a whale, there's a whalefish,' he
  cried,
'And she blows at every span' – brave boys,
  She blows at every span.

Our captain stood on his quarter-deck,
And a fine little man was he.
'Overhaul, overhaul, on your davit tackle fall,
And launch your boats to the sea' – brave boys,
  And launch your boats to the sea.

Now the boats were launched and the men a-board,
With the whalefish full in view;
Resol-ved were the whole boats' crews
To steer where the whalefish blew – brave boys,
　To steer where the whalefish blew.

And when we reached that whale, my boys,
He lashed out with his tail,
And we lost a boat, and seven good men,
And we never caught that whale – brave boys,
　And we never caught that whale.

Bad news, bad news, to our captain came,
That grieved him very sore.
But when he found that his cabin-boy was gone,
Why it grieved him ten times more – brave boys,
　It grieved him ten times more.

O, Greenland is an awful place,
Where the daylight's seldom seen,
Where there's ice, and there's snow, and the whalefishes
　blow,
Then *adieu* to cold Greenland – brave boys,
　Adieu to cold Greenland.

Unknown

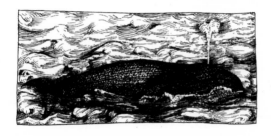

She was Poor but She was Honest

She was poor, but she was honest,
    Victim of the squire's whim:
First he loved her, then he left her,
    And she lost her honest name.

Then she ran away to London,
    For to hide her grief and shame;
There she met another squire,
    And she lost her name again.

See her riding in her carriage,
    In the Park and all so gay:
All the nibs and nobby persons
    Come to pass the time of day.

See the little old-world village
    Where her aged parents live,
Drinking the champagne she sends them;
    But they never can forgive.

In the rich man's arms she flutters,
    Like a bird with broken wing:
First he loved her, then he left her,
    And she hasn't got a ring.

See him in the splendid mansion,
    Entertaining with the best,
While the girl that he has ruined,
    Entertains a sordid guest.

See him in the House of Commons,
   Making laws to put down crime,
While the victim of his passions
   Trails her way through mud and slime.

Standing on the bridge at midnight,
   She says: 'Farewell, blighted Love.'
There's a scream, a splash – Good Heavens!
   What is she a-doing of?

Then they drag her from the river,
   Water from her clothes they wrang,
For they thought that she was drownded;
   But the corpse got up and sang:

'It's the same the whole world over,
   It's the poor that gets the blame,
It's the rich that gets the pleasure.
   Isn't it a blooming shame?'

Unknown

ou'd Better Believe Him
A Fable

Discovered an old rocking-horse in Woolworth's,
He tried to feed it but without much luck
So he stroked it, had a long conversation about
The trees it came from, the attics it had visited.
Tried to take it out then
But the store detective he
Called the police who in court next morning said
'He acted strangely when arrested,
His statement read simply "I believe in rocking-horses."
We have reason to believe him mad.'
'Quite so,' said the prosecution,
'Bring in the rocking-horse as evidence.'
'I'm afraid it's escaped, sir,' said the store manager,
'Left a hoof print as evidence
On the skull of the store detective.'
'Quite so,' said the prosecution, fearful
of the neighing
Out in the corridor.

Brian Patten

The Bishop's Mistake

The bishop glanced through his window pane
On a world of sleet, and wind, and rain.
When a dreary figure met his eyes
That made the bishop soliloquize.

And as the bishop gloomily thought
He ordered pen and ink to be brought.
Then 'Providence Watches' he plainly wrote
And pinned the remark to a one-pound note.

Seizing his hat from his lordly rack
And wrapping his cloak around his back,
Across the road the bishop ran
And gave the note to the shabby man.

That afternoon was the bishop's 'At Home',
When everyone gathered beneath his dome,
Curate and canon from far and near
Came to partake of the bishop's cheer.

There in the good old bishop's hall
Stood a stranger lean and tall.
'Your winnings, my lord,' he cried. 'Well done –
"Providence Watches", at ten to one.'

It is to be noted on Sunday next
The bishop skilfully chose his text.
And from the pulpit earnestly told
Of the fertile seed that returned tenfold.

Unknown

Ballad

Oh come, my joy, my soldier boy,
With your golden buttons, your scarlet coat,
Oh let me play with your twinkling sword
And sail away in your wonderful boat!

The soldier came and took the boy.
Together they marched the dusty roads.
Instead of war, they sang at Fairs,
And mended old chairs with river reeds.

The boy put on a little black patch
And learned to sing on a tearful note;
The soldier sold his twinkling sword
To buy a crutch and a jet-black flute.

And when the summer sun rode high
They laughed the length of the shining day;
But when the robin stood in the hedge
The little lad's courage drained away.

Oh soldier, my soldier, take me home
To the nut-brown cottage under the hill.
My mother is waiting, I'm certain sure;
She's far too old to draw at the well!

As snowflakes fell the boy spoke so,
For twenty years, ah twenty years;
But a look in the soldier's eyes said no,
And the roads of England were wet with tears.

One morning, waking on the moors,
The lad laughed loud at the corpse by his side.
He buried the soldier under a stone,
But kept the flute to soothe his pride.

The days dragged on and he came to a town,
Where he got a red jacket for chopping wood;
And meeting a madman by the way,
He bartered the flute for a twinkling sword.

And so he walked the width of the land
With a warlike air and a jaunty word,
Looking out for a likely lad,
With the head of a fool and the heart of a bard.

Henry Treece

The Listeners

'Is there anybody there?' said the Traveller,
   Knocking on the moonlit door;
And his horse in the silence champed the grasses
   Of the forest's ferny floor:
And a bird flew up out of the turret,
   Above the Traveller's head:
And he smote upon the door a second time;
   'Is there anybody there?' he said.
But no one descended to the Traveller;
   No head from the leaf-fringed sill
Leaned over and looked into his grey eyes,
   Where he stood perplexed and still.
But only a host of phantom listeners
   That dwelt in the lone house then
Stood listening in the quiet of the moonlight
   To that voice from the world of men:

Stood thronging the faint moonbeams on the dark stair,
  That goes down to the empty hall,
Hearkening in an air stirred and shaken
  By the lonely Traveller's call.
And he felt in his heart their strangeness,
  Their stillness answering his cry,
While his horse moved, cropping the dark turf,
  'Neath the starred and leafy sky;
For he suddenly smote on the door, even
  Louder, and lifted his head:
'Tell them I came, and no one answered,
  That I kept my word,' he said.
Never the least stir made the listeners
  Though every word he spake
Fell echoing through the shadowiness of the still house
  From the one man left awake:
Ay, they heard his foot upon the stirrup,
  And the sound of iron on stone,
And how the silence surged softly backward,
  When the plunging hoofs were gone.

Walter de la Mare

Jean Richepin's Song

A poor lad once and a lad so trim,
Fol de rol de raly O!
Fol de rol!
A poor lad once and a lad so trim
Gave his love to her that loved not him.

And, says she, 'Fetch me tonight, you rogue,'
Fol de rol de raly O!
Fol de rol!
And, says she, 'Fetch me tonight, you rogue,
Your mother's heart to feed my dog!'

To his mother's house went that young man,
Fol de rol de raly O!
Fol de rol!
To his mother's house went that young man,
Killed her, and took the heart, and ran.

And as he was running, look you, he fell,
Fol de rol de raly O!
Fol de rol!
And as he was running, look you, he fell,
And the heart rolled on the ground as well.

And the lad, as the heart was a-rolling, heard
Fol de rol de raly O!
Fol de rol!
And the lad, as the heart was a-rolling, heard
That the heart was speaking, and this was the word;

The heart was a-weeping, and crying so small
Fol de rol de raly O!
Fol de rol!
The heart was a-weeping, and crying so small,
'Are you hurt, my child, are you hurt at all?'

Herbert Trench

The Dorking Thigh

About to marry and invest
   Their lives in safety and routine,
Stanley and June required a nest
   And came down on the 4.15.

The agent drove them to the Posh Estate
   And showed them several habitations.
None did. The afternoon got late
   With questions, doubts, and explanations.

Then day grew dim and Stan fatigued
   And disappointment raised its head,
But June declared herself intrigued
   To know where that last turning led.

It led to a Tudor snuggery styled
   YE KUMFI NOOKLET on the gate.
'A gem of a home,' the salesman smiled,
   'My pet place on the whole estate;

It's not quite finished, but you'll see
   Good taste itself.' They went inside.
'This little place is built to be
   A husband's joy, a housewife's pride.'

They saw the white convenient sink,
   The modernistic chimneypiece.
June gasped for joy, Stan gave a wink
   To say, 'Well, here our quest can cease.'

The salesman purred (he'd managed well)
    And June undid a cupboard door.
'For linen,' she beamed. And out there fell
    A nameless Something on the floor.

'Something the workmen left, I expect,'
    The agent said, as it fell at his feet,
Nor knew that his chance of a sale was wrecked.
    'Good heavens, it must be a joint of meat!'

Ah yes, it was meat, it was meat all right,
    A joint those three will never forget –
For they stood alone in the Surrey night
    With the severed thigh of a plump brunette ...

*   *   *

Early and late, early and late,
    Traffic was jammed round the Posh Estate,
And the papers were full of the Dorking Thigh
    And who, and when, and where, and why.

A trouser button was found in the mud.
    (Who made it? Who wore it? Who lost it? Who knows?)
But no one found a trace of blood
    Or her body or face, or the spoiler of those.

He's acting a play in the common air
    On which no curtain can ever come down.
Though YE KUMFI NOOKLET was shifted elsewhere
    June made Stan take a flat in town.

William Plomer

The Death of Romeo and Juliet

Romeo rode to the sepulchre, 'mong dead folks, bats, and
    creepers;
And swallowed down the burning dose – when Juliet oped
    her peepers.
'Are you alive? Or is't your ghost? Speak quick, before I go.'
'Alive!' she cried, 'and kicking too; art thou my Romeo?'
'It is your Romeo, my faded little blossum;
O Juliet! is it possible that you were acting possum?'
'I was indeed; now let's go home; pa's spite will have abated;
What ails you love, you stagger so; are you intoxicated?'
'No, no, my duck; I took some stuff that caused a little fit;'
He struggled hard to tell her all, but couldn't, so he quit.
In shorter time than't takes a lamb to wag his tail, or jump,
Poor Romeo was stiff and pale as any whitewashed pump.
Then Juliet seized that awful knife, and in her bosom stuck
    it,
Let out a most terrific yell, fell down, and kicked the bucket.

Unknown

Charity

While once in haste I crossed the street,
  A little girl I saw,
Deep in the mud she'd placed her feet,
  And gazed on me with awe.

'Dear sir,' with trembling tone she said,
  'Here have I stood for weeks,
And never had a bit of bread,'
  Here tears bedewed her cheeks.

'Poor child!' said I, 'do you stand here,
  And quickly will I buy
Some wholesome bread and strengthening beer,
  And fetch it speedily.'

Off ran I to the baker's shop,
  As hard as I could pelt,
Fearing 'twas late, I made a stop,
  And in my pocket felt.

In my left pocket did I seek,
  To see how time went on,
Then grief and tears bedewed *my* cheek,
  For oh! my watch was gone!

Lewis Carroll

The Wild Colonial Boy

There was a wild colonial boy, Jack Donahoe by name,
Of poor but honest parents he was born in Castlemaine.
He was his father's dearest hope, his mother's pride and joy.
O, fondly did his parents love their Wild Colonial Boy.

So ride with me, my hearties, we'll cross the mountains high.
Together we will plunder, together we will die.
We'll wander through the valleys and gallop o'er the plains,
For we scorn to live in slavery, bound down with iron chains!

He was scarcely sixteen years of age when he left his father's
    home,
A convict to Australia, across the seas to roam.
They put him in the Iron Gang in the Government employ,
But ne'er an iron on earth could hold the Wild Colonial
    Boy.

And when they sentenced him to hang to end his wild career,
With a loud shout of defiance bold Donahoe broke clear.
He robbed those wealthy squatters, their stock he did
    destroy,
But never a trap in the land could catch the Wild Colonial
    Boy.

Then one day when he was cruising near the broad Nepean's
    side,
From out the thick Bringelly bush the horse police did ride.
'Die or resign, Jack Donahoe!' they shouted in their joy.
'I'll fight this night with all my might!' cried the Wild
    Colonial Boy.

He fought six rounds with the horse police before the fatal
    ball,
Which pierced his heart with cruel smart, caused Donahoe
    to fall.
And then he closed his mournful eyes, his pistol an empty
    toy,
Crying, 'Parents dear, O say a prayer for the Wild Colonial
    Boy.'

Unknown

Jock of Hazeldean

'Why weep ye by the tide, ladie?
   Why weep ye by the tide?
I'll wed ye to my youngest son,
   And ye sall be his bride:
And ye sall be his bride, ladie,
   Sae comely to be seen' –
But aye she loot the tears down fa'
   For Jock of Hazeldean.

'Now let this wilfu' grief be done,
   And dry that cheek so pale;
Young Frank is chief of Errington,
   And lord of Langley-dale;
His step is first in peaceful ha',
   His sword in battle keen' –
But aye she loot the tears down fa'
   For Jock of Hazeldean.

'A chain of gold ye sall not lack,
    Nor braid to bind your hair;
Nor mettled hound, nor managed hawk,
    Nor palfrey fresh and fair;
And you, the foremost o' them a',
    Shall ride our forest queen' –
But aye she loot the tears down fa'
    For Jock of Hazeldean.

The kirk was decked at morning-tide,
    The tapers glimmered fair;
The priest and bridegroom wait the bride,
    And dame and knight are there.
They sought her baith by bower and ha';
    The ladie was not seen!
She's o'er the Border, and awa'
    Wi' Jock of Hazeldean.

Sir Walter Scott

The Mistletoe Bough

The mistletoe hung in the castle hall,
The holly branch shone on the old oak wall;
And the baron's retainers were blithe and gay,
And keeping their Christmas holiday.
The baron beheld with a father's pride
His beautiful child, young Lovell's bride;
While she with her bright eyes seemed to be
The star of the goodly company.

'I'm weary of dancing now,' she cried;
'Here tarry a moment – I'll hide – I'll hide!
And, Lovell, be sure thou'rt first to trace
The clue to my secret lurking place.'
Away she ran – and her friends began
Each tower to search, and each nook to scan;
And young Lovell cried, 'Oh where dost thou hide?
I'm lonesome without thee, my own dear bride.'
They sought her that night! and they sought her next day!
And they sought her in vain when a week passed away!
In the highest – the lowest – the loneliest spot,
Young Lovell sought wildly – but found her not.
And years flew by, and their grief at last
Was told as a sorrowful tale long past,
And when Lovell appeared, the children cried,
'See! the old man weeps for his fairy bride.'

At length an oak chest, that had long lain hid,
Was found in the castle – they raised the lid –
And a skeleton form lay mouldering there,
In the bridal wreath of that lady fair!
Oh! sad was her fate! – in sportive jest
She hid from her lord in the old oak chest.
It closed with a spring! and, dreadful doom,
The bride lay clasped in her living tomb!

Thomas Haynes Bayly

Heriot's Ford

'What's that that hirples at my side?'
The foe that you must fight, my lord.
'That rides as fast as I can ride?'
The shadow of your might, my lord.

'Then wheel my horse against the foe!'
He's down and overpast, my lord.
You war against the sunset-glow,
The judgement follows fast, my lord!

'Oh, who will stay the sun's descent?'
King Joshua he is dead, my lord.
'I need an hour to repent!'
'Tis what our sister said, my lord.

'Oh, do not slay me in my sins!'
You're safe awhile with us, my lord.
'Nay, kill me ere my fear begins!'
We would not serve you thus, my lord.

'Where is the doom that I must face?'
Three little leagues away, my lord.
'Then mend the horses' laggard pace!'
We need them for next day, my lord.

'Next day – next day! Unloose my cords!'
Our sister needed none, my lord.
You had no mind to face our swords,
And – where can cowards run, my lord?

'You would not kill the soul alive?'
'Twas thus our sister cried, my lord.
'I dare not die with none to shrive.'
But so our sister died, my lord.

'Then wipe the sweat from brow and cheek.'
It runnels forth afresh, my lord.
'Uphold me – for the flesh is weak.'
You've finished with the Flesh, my lord!

Rudyard Kipling

hirples walks lamely, hobbles

Friday Morning

It was on a Friday morning that they took me from the cell,
And I saw they had a carpenter to crucify as well:
You can blame it on to Pilate, you can blame it on the Jews,
You can blame it on the devil, but it's God I accuse.

'It's God they ought to crucify instead of you and me,'
I said it to the carpenter a-hanging on the tree.

You can blame it on to Adam, you can blame it on to Eve,
You can blame it on the apple, but that I can't believe;
It was God who made the devil and the woman and the
man,
But there wouldn't be an apple if it wasn't in the plan.

Now Barabbas was a killer, and they let Barabbas go,
But you are being crucified for nothing here below,
And God is up in heaven, but he doesn't do a thing,
With a million angels watching, and they never move a
wing.

'To hell with Jehovah!' to the carpenter I said,
'I wish that a carpenter had made the world instead.
Good-bye and good luck to you, our ways they will divide,
Remember me in heaven, the man you hung beside.'

Sidney Carter

Meeting at Night

The grey sea and the long black land;
And the yellow half-moon large and low.
And the startled little waves that leap
In fiery ringlets from their sleep,
As I gain the cove with pushing prow,
And quench its speed i' the slushy sand.

Then a mile of warm sea-scented beach;
Three fields to cross till a farm appears;
A tap at the pane, the quick sharp scratch
And blue spurt of a lighted match,
And a voice less loud, through its joys and fears,
Than the two hearts beating each to each!

Robert Browning

Welsh Incident

'But that was nothing to what things came out
From the sea-caves of Criccieth yonder.'
'What were they? Mermaids? dragons? ghosts?'
'Nothing at all of any things like that.'
'What were they, then?'
                                'All sorts of queer things,
Things never seen or heard or written about,
Very strange, un-Welsh, utterly peculiar
Things. Oh, solid enough they seemed to touch,
Had anyone dared it. Marvellous creation,
All various shapes and sizes, and no sizes,
All new, each perfectly unlike his neighbour,
Though all came moving slowly out together.'
'Describe just one of them.'
                                'I am unable.'
'What were their colours?'
                                'Mostly nameless colours,
Colours you'd like to see; but one was puce
Or perhaps more like crimson, but not purplish.
Some had no colour.'
                                'Tell me, had they legs?'
'Not a leg nor foot among them that I saw.'
'But did these things come out in any order?
What o'clock was it? What was the day of the week?
Who else was present? How was the weather?'
'I was coming to that. It was half-past three
On Easter Tuesday last. The sun was shining.
The Harlech Silver Band played "Marchog Jesu"
On thirty-seven shimmering instruments,
Collecting for Caernarvon's (Fever) Hospital Fund.

The populations of Pwllheli, Criccieth,
Portmadoc, Borth, Tremadoc, Penrhyndeudraeth,
Were all assembled. Criccieth's mayor addressed them
First in good Welsh and then in fluent English,
Twisting his fingers in his chain of office,
Welcoming the things. They came out on the sand,
Not keeping time to the band, moving seaward
Silently at a snail's pace. But at last
The most odd, indescribable thing of all,
Which hardly one man there could see for wonder,
Did something recognizably a something.'
'Well, what?'
            'It made a noise.'
                      'A frightening noise?'
'No, no.'
       'A musical noise? A noise of scuffling?'
'No, but a very loud, respectable noise –
Like groaning to oneself on Sunday morning
In Chapel, close before the second psalm.'
'What did the mayor do?'
                  'I was coming to that.'

Robert Graves

O What is That Sound

O what is that sound which so thrills the ear
   Down in the valley drumming, drumming?
Only the scarlet soldiers, dear,
   The soldiers coming.

O what is that light I see flashing so clear
   Over the distance brightly, brightly?
Only the sun on their weapons, dear,
   As they step lightly.

O what are they doing with all that gear;
   What are they doing this morning, this morning?
Only the usual manoeuvres, dear,
   Or perhaps a warning.

O why have they left the road down there;
   Why are they suddenly wheeling, wheeling?
Perhaps a change in the orders, dear;
   Why are you kneeling?

O haven't they stopped for the doctor's care;
   Haven't they reined their horses, their horses?
Why, they are none of them wounded, dear,
   None of these forces.

O is it the parson they want with white hair;
   Is it the parson, is it, is it?
No, they are passing his gateway, dear,
   Without a visit.

O it must be the farmer who lives so near;
   It must be the farmer so cunning, so cunning?
They have passed the farm already, dear,
   And now they are running.

O where are you going? stay with me here!
   Were the vows you swore me deceiving, deceiving?
No, I promised to love you, dear,
   But I must be leaving.

O it's broken the lock and splintered the door,
   O it's the gate where they're turning, turning;
Their feet are heavy on the floor
   And their eyes are burning.

                    W. H. Auden

Legend

I saw three ships go sailing by,
Over the sea, the lifting sea,
And the wind rose in the morning sky,
And one was rigged for a long journey.

The first ship turned towards the west,
Over the sea, the running sea,
And by the wind was all possessed
And carried to a rich country.

The second turned towards the east,
Over the sea, the quaking sea,
And the wind hunted it like a beast
To anchor in captivity.

The third ship drove towards the north,
Over the sea, the darkening sea,
But no breath of wind came forth,
And the decks shone frostily.

The northern sky rose high and black
Over the proud unfruitful sea,
East and west the ships came back
Happily or unhappily:

But the third went wide and far
Into an unforgiving sea
Under a fire-spilling star,
And it was rigged for a long journey.

Philip Larkin

The Old Pilot's Death

He discovers himself on an old airfield.
He thinks he was there before,
but rain has washed out the lettering of a sign.
A single biplane, all struts and wires,
stands in the long grass and wildflowers.
He pulls himself into the narrow cockpit
although his muscles are stiff
and sits like an egg in a nest of canvas.
He sees that the machine gun has rusted.
The glass over the instruments
has broken, and the red arrows are gone
from his gas gauge and his altimeter.
When he looks up, his propeller is turning,
although no one was there to snap it.
He lets out the throttle. The engine catches
and the propeller spins into the wind.
He bumps over holes in the grass,
and he remembers to pull back on the stick.
He rises from the land in a high bounce
which gets higher, and suddenly he is flying again.
He feels the old fear, and rising over the fields
the old gratitude. In the distance, circling
in a beam of late sun like birds migrating,
there are the wings of a thousand biplanes.
He banks and flies to join them.

Donald Hall
in memory of Philip Thompson, d. 1960

To Find a Son and Heir
A Story from Zimbabwe

A wrinkled father, more like a tortoise than
   (what in fact he was) a rich old man,
sent word that his twin sons should come to the bed
   on which he'd shortly die, and said:
'My sons, since you are twins, I've set a test
   to settle which of you had best
inherit my great fortune. Here's ten pounds
   each. Now then, I've built in the grounds
two empty rooms, identical in size,
   and whichever of you is wise
enough to fill his room chock-full, yet still
   have change out of the ten pounds, will
be heir to all I have.' Now apprehensive
   of each other, the twins grew pensive
and sloped off to the dark forest's glades where
   they pondered how they should prepare
themselves for the next day's trial. Their neighbours,
   taking a holiday from their labours,
crowded about the two rooms, squinnying through
   each slit, crack, hole in order to
see which of the twins would come up with the answer.
   The first (hard-headed and no romancer)
drives up with a huge lorryful of sacks,
   crates, cartons, boxes, which he stacks
in every nook and cranny, only to discover
   that there are yawning gaps all over
and not the ghost of a hope of plugging any
   of them with his remaining penny.

All eyes now turn towards the second son,
    a dreamy youth, who hasn't done
a blind bit (so it seems) to get things ready,
    but keeps his cool amid the heady
jeers of the crowd. Entering the empty room,
    he gropes through the thronging shadows' gloom
to its still heart. There, placing it upright,
    he sets a penny candle alight,
whose beams spread out in a golden dawn
    to fill, flood and scour like a sun reborn
the room's small universe ... The crowd, grown quiet,
    begin to understand and riot,
clapping and cheering as, shoulder-high, they bear
    to the sick father his true son and heir.

Raymond Wilson

Is My Team Ploughing

'Is my team ploughing,
    That I was used to drive
And hear the harness jingle
    When I was man alive?'

Ay, the horses trample,
    The harness jingles now;
No change though you lie under
    The land you used to plough.

'Is football playing
    Along the river shore,
With lads to chase the leather,
    Now I stand up no more?'

Ay, the ball is flying,
    The lads play heart and soul;
The goal stands up, the keeper
    Stands up to keep the goal.

'Is my girl happy,
    That I thought hard to leave,
And has she tired of weeping
    As she lies down at eve?'

Ay, she lies down lightly,
    She lies not down to weep:
Your girl is well contented.
    Be still, my lad, and sleep.

'Is my friend hearty,
    Now I am thin and pine,
And has he found to sleep in
    A better bed than mine?'

Yes, lad, I lie easy,
    I lie as lads would choose;
I cheer a dead man's sweetheart,
    Never ask me whose.

A. E. Housman

Bedtime Story

A giant ant is telling a bedtime story to one of its children. The story is
the legend of how the last man was accidentally wiped out by a Mission
Patrol wishing to help him.

Long long ago when the world was a wild place
Planted with bushes and peopled by apes, our
Mission Brigade was at work in the jungle.
     Hard by the Congo

Once, when a foraging detail was active
Scouting for green-fly, it came on a grey man, the
Last living man, in the branch of a baobab
     Stalking a monkey.

Earlier men had disposed of, for pleasure,
Creatures whose names we scarcely remember –
Zebra, rhinoceros, elephants, wart-hog,
     Lions, rats, deer. But

After the wars had extinguished the cities
Only the wild ones were left, half-naked
Near the Equator: and here was the last one,
     Starved for a monkey.

By then the Mission Brigade had encountered
Hundreds of such men; and their procedure,
History tells us, was only to feed them:
     Find them and feed them;

Those were the orders. And this was the last one.
Nobody knew that he was, but he was. Mud
Caked on his flat grey flanks. He was crouched, half-
    armed with a shaved spear

Glinting beneath broad leaves. When their jaws cut
Swathes through the bark and he saw fine teeth shine,
Round eyes roll round and forked arms waver
    Huge as the rough trunks

Over his head, he was frightened. Our workers
Marched through the Congo before he was born, but
This was the first time perhaps that he'd seen one.
    Staring in hot still

Silence, he crouched there: then jumped. With a long swing
Down from his branch, he had angled his spear too
Quickly, before they could hold him, and hurled it
    Hard at the soldier

Leading the detail. How could he know Queen's
Orders were only to help him? The soldier
Winced when the tipped spear pricked him. Unsheathing
  his
    Sting was a reflex.

Later the Queen was informed. There were no more
Men. An impetuous soldier had killed off,
Purely by chance, the penultimate primate.
    When she was certain,

Squadrons of workers were fanned through the Congo
Detailed to bring back the man's picked bones to be
Sealed in the archives in amber. I'm quite sure
      Nobody found them

After the most industrious search, though.
Where had the bones gone? Over the earth, dear,
Ground by the teeth of the termites, blown by the
      Wind, like the dodo's.

                              George MacBeth

Henry King
who chewed bits of string and was early cut off in dreadful agonies

The chief defect of Henry King
Was chewing little bits of string.
At last he swallowed some which tied
Itself in ugly knots inside.
Physicians of the utmost fame
Were called at once; but when they came
They answered, as they took their fees,
'There is no cure for this disease.
Henry will very soon be dead.'
His parents stood about his bed
Lamenting his untimely death,
When Henry, with his latest breath,
Cried – 'Oh, my friends, be warned by me,
That breakfast, dinner, lunch and tea
Are all the human frame requires ...'
With that the wretched child expires.

Hilaire Belloc

Tom's Angel

No one was in the fields
But me and Polly Flint,
When, like a giant across the grass,
The flaming angel went.

It was budding time in May,
And green as green could be,
And all in his height he went along
Past Polly Flint and me.

We'd been playing in the woods,
And Polly up, and ran,
And hid her face, and said,
'Tom! Tom! The Man! The Man!'

And I up-turned; and there,
Like flames across the sky,
With wings all bristling, came
The Angel striding by.

And a chaffinch overhead
Kept whistling in the tree
While the Angel, blue as fire, came on
Past Polly Flint and me.

And I saw his hair, and all
The ruffling of his hem,
As over the clovers his bare feet
Trod without stirring them.

Polly – she cried; and, oh!
We ran, until the lane
Turned by the miller's roaring wheel,
And we were safe again.

Walter de la Mare

The Outlandish Knight

An outlandish knight from the North lands came,
   And he came a-wooing to me;
He promised he'd take me to the North lands
   And there he'd marry me.

'Come fetch me some of your father's gold,
   And some of your mother's fee,
And two of the best nags in the stable,
   Where there stand thirty and three.'

She's mounted on the milk-white steed,
   And he on the dappled grey;
They rode till they came unto the sea-side,
   Three hours before it was day.

'Light off, light off thy milk-white steed,
   And deliver him unto me;
For six pretty maids have I drowned here
   And thou the seventh shall be.

'Pull off, pull off thy silken gown
   And deliver it unto me;
It is too fine and too rich a gear
   To rot in the salt, salt sea.

'Pull off, pull off thy Holland smock,
   And deliver it unto me;
It is too fine and too rich a gear
   To rot in the salt, salt sea.'

'If I must take off my Holland smock,
    Then turn your back to me;
It is not fitting that such a ruffian
    A naked woman should see.'

He'd turned his face away from her,
    And viewed the leaves so green;
She's catched him by the middle so small
    And she's tumbled him into the stream.

'Lie there, lie there, false-hearted man,
    Lie there instead of me;
For if six pretty maids thou hast drowned here,
    The seventh one hath drowned thee.'

She's mounted on the milk-white steed,
    And she led the dappled grey;
She rode till she came to her own father's hall,
    Three hours before it was day.

The parrot being in the window so high,
    Hearing the lady, did say,
'I'm afraid some ruffian has led you astray,
    That you've tarried so long away.'

'Don't prattle, don't prattle, my pretty Polly,
    Nor tell any tales on me;
And your cage shall be made of the glittering gold,
    And the door of the best ivory.'

Unknown

Little Billee

There were three sailors of Bristol city
Who took a boat and went to sea.
But first with beef and captain's biscuits
And pickled pork they loaded she.

There was gorging Jack and guzzling Jimmy,
And the youngest he was little Billee.
Now when they got as far as the Equator
They'd nothing left but one split pea.

Says gorging Jack to guzzling Jimmy,
'I am extremely hungaree.'
To gorging Jack says guzzling Jimmy,
'We've nothing left, us must eat we.'

Says gorging Jack to guzzling Jimmy,
'With one another we shouldn't agree!
There's little Bill, he's young and tender,
We're old and tough, so let's eat he.

'Oh! Billy, we're going to kill and eat you,
So undo the button of your chemie.'
When Bill received this information
He used his pocket handkerchie.

'First let me say my catechism,
Which my poor mammy taught to me.'
'Make haste, make haste,' says guzzling Jimmy,
While Jack pulled out his snickersnee.

So Billy went up to the maintop gallant mast,
And down he fell on his bended knee.
He scarce had come to the twelfth commandment
When up he jumps. 'There's land I see:

'Jerusalem and Madagascar,
And North and South Amerikee:
There's the British flag a-riding at anchor,
With Admiral Napier, KCB.'

So when they got aboard of the Admiral's
He hanged fat Jack and flogged Jimmee;
But as for little Bill he made him
The Captain of a Seventy-three.

William Makepeace Thackeray

The Pursuit

Trample! trample! went the roan,
    Trap! trap! went the grey;
But pad! pad! PAD! like a thing that was mad,
    My chestnut broke away.
It was just five miles from Salisbury town,
    And but one hour to day.

Thud! THUD! came on the heavy roan,
    Rap! rap! the mottled grey;
But my chestnut mare was of blood so rare,
    That she showed them all the way.
Spur on! spur on! – I doffed my hat,
    And wished them all good-day.

They splashed through miry rut and pool,
    Splintered through fence and rail;
But chestnut Kate switched over the gate –
    I saw them droop and tail.
To Salisbury town, but a mile of down,
    Once over this brook and rail.

Trap! trap! I heard their echoing hoofs
    Past the walls of mossy stone;
The roan flew on with a staggering pace,
    But blood is better than bone.
I patted old Kate, and gave her the spur,
    For I knew it was all my own.

But trample! trample! came their steeds,
  And I saw their wolf's eyes burn;
I felt like a royal hart at bay,
  And made me ready to turn.
I looked where the highest grew the may,
  And deepest arched the fern.

I flew at the first knave's sallow throat;
  One blow, and he was down.
The second rogue fired twice, and missed;
  I sliced the villain's crown,
Clove through the rest, and flogged brave Kate,
  Fast, fast, to Salisbury town!

Pad! pad! they came on the level sward,
  THUD! THUD! upon the sand;
With a gleam of swords, and a burning match,
  And a shaking of flag and hand:
But one long bound, and I passed the gate,
  Safe, safe, from the canting band.

G. W. Thornbury

The Destined Hour

To Abou Seyd his servant came, Hussein,
    With ashen lips – 'O Master, let me go
Home to Samarra – I would come again
      In three days' space.'
Then, with a smile upon his sword-scarred face,
    The old Seyd answered: 'Son, what drives thee so?
    Some sudden trouble? Nay, I need not know.
For Allah is the Lord of all men's ways.'

'O Master, listen – I will tell thee why.
    In our bazaar but now I saw there stood
A stranger, tall and silent. Passing by,
    I peered into his face. But ah, my breath
      Failed. For beneath his hood
Two eyes burned – hollow. Master, it was
    Death!
He raised his hand to strike. Oh let me fly! –
Though Allah is the Lord of all men's days.'

Then Abou Seyd, old captain that had seen
    A hundred times across the battle glide
The face of Death, inclined his head, serene;
    And Hussein vanished through the columned court.
      But laying God's word aside,
    Across the noonday glare his Master sought
    The buzz of the bazaar. 'Poor fool!' he thought.
'Yet Allah is the Lord of all men's ways.'

Loud swarmed the buyers round each booth and stall;
   But there by Omar's Mosque, at the market's end,
Watched one shape like a shadow, gaunt and tall.
   Then, drawing near, said Abou Seyd, 'My friend,
Why threaten my poor slave – so wantonly –
      That harmed thee not at all?
In my hot youth I might have threatened *thee*,
Forgetting Allah, Lord of all men's days.'

Then that dark face upon him bent such eyes,
   The scar upon Seyd's cheek grew grey with fear.
'I threatened not thy servant, Abou Seyd.
      But in surprise
   I raised my hand, to see him standing near.
For this same night God bids my hand be laid
   Upon him at Samarra, far from here.
Yet Allah is the Lord of all men's ways.'

F. L. Lucas

The Wily Astrologer

A beggar demanded to see the king,
   claiming that he could do more
to find out where his majesty's lost ring
lay hid than astrologers by the score
and all the wise men of the court had been able to do
   heretofore.

'Notwithstanding these rags in which I stand,
   I can sus out the stars at a glance,
and all I'd ask at your majesty's hand
is a warm room, some magical books, and the chance
to eat all the best food in Italy, washed down by the best
   wines of France.'

'Just see that you do as he asks,' warned the king,
   tilting his nose from the reek of him.
'Since there's nobody here who can find the ring,
let's give him his head, for I quite like the cheek of him;
and from such plain speaking I cannot suspect the least
   thing that's oblique of him.'

He was served the choicest of wine and food,
   and fumbled an old book or so;
but the notes that he scribbled were not understood,
which was hardly surprising, since he didn't know
one word from the next, or the twinkling stars from a firefly's
   soft glow.

What he *could* read was human nature, and
   he soon asked himself just why
all the servants ran scampering at his command,
called him 'Sir', or 'Master' or even 'My
Lord Wizard'. Could it be they were hiding something for
   fear he might pry?

So he secretly sent for his beggar wife
   and hid her under his bed,
with instructions to frighten out of his life
each servant who entered. 'Speak low,' he said,
'and accusingly, and make sure that you sound like the voice
   of the dead.'

Which she did, as each servant came into the room,
    saying, 'Here comes a guilty man!'
in a low, dark voice, like a voice from the tomb,
and their hair stood on end, and they turned and ran,
begging the beggar for pardon, so that all went according
    to plan.

'If you promise,' they said, 'not to tell the king,
    you can have a whole bagful of gold.'
'Agreed,' said the beggar, 'but first take the ring
smeared with honey and meal, and make sure that the old
tattered turkey gobbles it up. Now clear off, and do as you're
    told!'

Which they did. Then the beggar sent word to the king
    how he knew by astrology
that the turkey's crop contained the lost ring;
and though the wise men scoffed in their college, he
forced the whole lot to eat their own words with a full-
    blooded apology.

The king gave command that the turkey's crop should be
    slit for all to behold,
and the ring was found as the beggar said it would be;
then he claimed his reward, took his wife and his gold
and his leave of the king – as of this story, now that all of
    it's told.

Raymond Wilson

Highwayman's Hollow

'Where the cliff hangs hollow, where the gloom falls chill,
You hear a something, follow, follow, follow down the hill;
Where the horses sweat and lather and the dusk begins to
gather,
It is there that I will meet you and will greet you,
            You, Sir Traveller.'

'Where the leaves lie rotting and the night falls blind,
You hear a someone trotting, trotting, trotting down the
wind,
And you listen all a-shiver to my ghostly "Stand, deliver,"
Yes, although my bones have whitened, you are frightened
            Yet, Sir Traveller.'

"Twas a traveller who slew me where the dark firs frown,
'Twas his small sword through me and the blood dripped
down.
Where the horses sweat and lather and the dusk begins to
gather,
It is there I ride behind you to remind you,
            You, Sir Traveller.'

Gilbert V. Yonge

The Demon Lover

'Well met, well met, my own true-love;
    Long time I have been absent from thee.
I'm lately come from the salt sea,
    And it's all for the sake, my love, of thee.

'I have three ships all on the sea,
    And one of them has brought me to land;
I've four and twenty seamen on board;
    And you shall have music at your command.'

She says: 'I'm now wed to a ship-carpenter,
    To a ship-carpenter I am bound,
And I wouldn't leave my husband dear
    For twice the sum of ten hundred pound.'

He says: 'I might have had a king's daughter,
    And fain she would have married me;
But I forsook her crown of gold,
    And it was all for the sake, my love, of thee.

'So I pray you leave your husband dear
    And sail away with me;
And I'll take you where them white lilies grow
    All on the banks of Italy.

'And the ship wherein my love shall sail
    Is wondrous to behold;
The sails shall be of shining silk
    And the masts shall be of red beaten gold.'

So she dressed herself in her gay clothing
    Most glorious to behold;
And as she trod that salt water side
    She shone like glittering gold.

Now they hadn't sailed a day and a day
    And a day but barely three,
When she cast herself down on the deck
    And wept and wailed most bitterly.

'Oh, hold your tongue, my dearest love,
    Let all your sorrows be.
For I'll take you where them white lilies grow
    All on the bottom of the sea.'

And as she turned herself round about,
    So tall and tall he seemed to be,
Until the tops of that gallant ship
    No taller were than he.

And he struck the topmast with his hand,
    The mainmast with his knee,
And he broke that shining ship in two
    And dashed it in the bottom of the sea.

Unknown

from The Emigrants
2. Columbus

Columbus from his after-
deck watched stars, absorbed in water,
melt in liquid amber drifting

through my summer air.
Now with morning, shadows lifting,
beaches stretched before him cold and clear.

Birds circled flapping flag and mizzen
mast: birds harshly hawking, without fear.
Discovery he sailed for was so near.

Columbus from his after-
deck watched heights he hoped for,
rocks he dreamed, rise solid from my simple water.

Parrots screamed. Soon he would touch
our land, his charted mind's desire.
The blue sky blessed the morning with its fire.

But did his vision
fashion, as he watched the shore,
the slaughter that his soldiers

furthered here? Pike
point and musket butt,
hot splintered courage, bones

cracked with bullet shot,
tipped black boot in my belly; the
whip's uncurled desire?

Columbus from his after-
deck saw bearded fig trees, yellow pouis
blazed like pollen and thin

waterfalls suspended in the green
as his eyes climbed towards the highest ridges
where our farms were hidden.

Now he was sure
he heard soft voices mocking in the leaves.
What did this journey mean, this
new world mean: dis-
covery? Or a return to terrors
he had sailed from, known before?

I watched him pause.

Then he was splashing silence.
Crabs snapped their claws
and scattered as he walked towards our shore.

Edward Kamau Brathwaite

pouis kind of coco with yellow root-stock

The Identification

So you think its Stephen?
Then I'd best make sure
Be on the safe side as it were.
Ah, theres been a mistake. The hair
you see, its black, now Stephens fair ...
What's that? The explosion?
Of course, burnt black. Silly of me.
I should have known. Then lets get on.

The face, is that a face I ask?
That mask of charred wood
blistered, scarred could
that have been a child's face?
The sweater, where intact, looks
in fact all too familiar.
But one must be sure.

The scoutbelt. Yes thats his.
I recognize the studs he hammered in
not a week ago. At the age
when boys get clothes-conscious
now you know. It's almost
certainly Stephen. But one must
be sure. Remove all trace of doubt.

Pockets. Empty the pockets.
Handkerchief? Could be any schoolboy's.
Dirty enough. Cigarettes?
Oh this can't be Stephen.
I dont allow him to smoke you see.
He wouldn't disobey me. Not his father.

But thats his penknife. Thats his alright.
And thats his key on the keyring
Gran gave him just the other night.
So this must be him.

I think I know what happened
... about the cigarettes
No doubt he was minding them
for one of the older boys.
Yes thats it.
Thats him.
Thats our Stephen.

                Roger McGough

Roll a Rock Down

Oh, out in the West where the riders are ready,
   They sing an old song and they tell an old tale,
And its moral is plain: Take it easy, go steady,
   While riding a horse on the Malibu Trail.

It's a high rocky trail with its switch-backs and doubles,
   It has no beginning and never an end:
It's risky and rough and it's plumb full of troubles,
   From Shifty – that's shale – up to Powder Cut Bend.

Old timers will tell you the rangers who made it
   Sang 'Roll a Rock Down' with a stiff upper lip
And cussed all creation, but managed to grade it;
   With a thousand-foot drop if a pony should slip.

Oh, the day it was wet and the sky it was cloudy,
   The trail was as slick as an oil-rigger's pants,
When Ranger McCabe on his pony, Old Rowdy,
   Came ridin' where walkin' was takin' a chance.

'Oh, Roll a Rock Down!' picks and shovels were clangin',
   And Rowdy a-steppin' that careful and light,
When the edge it gave way and McCabe was left hangin',
   Clean over the rim – with no bottom in sight.

I shook out a loop – bein' crowded for throwin';
   I flipped a fair noose for a rope that was wet:
It caught just as Mac lost his hold and was goin',
   And burned through my fingers: it's burnin' them yet.

For Ranger McCabe never knuckled to danger;
    My pardner in camp, on the trail, or in town:
And he slid into glory, a true forest-ranger,
    With: 'Hell! I'm a-goin'! Just roll a rock down.'

So, roll a rock down where a ranger is sleepin'
    Aside of his horse below Powder Cut Bend:
I ride and I look where the shadows are creepin',
    And roll a rock down – for McCabe was my friend.

I've sung you my song and I've told you my story,
    And all that I ask when I'm done with the show,
Is, roll a rock down when I slide into glory,
    And say that I went like a ranger should go.

Henry Herbert Knibbs

Lowery Cot

This is the house where Jesse White
Run staring in one misty night,
And said he seed the Holy Ghost
Out to Lowery finger-post.

Said It rised up like a cloud
Muttering to Itself out loud,
And stood tremendous on the hill
While all the breathing world was still.

They put en shivering to bed,
And in three days the man was dead.
Gert solemn visions such as they
Be overstrong for mortal clay.

L. A. G. Strong

An Accommodating Lion

An Athlete, one vacation,
Met a Lion in privation
On a desert where the lion-food was rare.
The Lion was delighted
That the Athlete he had sighted,
But the Athlete wished that he had been elsewhere.

The Athlete dared not fight him,
And he recalled an item
That was published in some journal he had read,
Of a lion that retreated,
Disheartened and defeated,
When an unarmed hunter stood upon his head.

On this hint from print extracted
The Athlete promptly acted,
And brandished both his shoe-heels high in air.
Upon his feat amazing
The Lion sat a-gazing,
And studied the phenomenon with care.

Said the Lion: 'This position
Is quite against tradition,
But I'll gladly eat you any way you choose;
Inverted perpendicular
Will do – I'm not particular!'
He finished him, beginning with his shoes.

Tudor Jenks

Hohenlinden

On Linden, when the sun was low,
All bloodless lay the untrodden snow
And dark as winter was the flow
    Of Iser, rolling rapidly.

But Linden saw another sight
When the drum beat at dead of night,
Commanding fires of death to light
    The darkness of her scenery.

By torch and trumpet fast arrayed,
Each horseman drew his battle-blade,
And furious every charger neighed
    To join the dreadful revelry.

Then shook the hills with thunder riven;
Then rushed the steed to battle driven;
And louder than the bolts of Heaven
    Far flashed the red artillery.

But redder yet that light shall glow
On Linden's hills of stainèd snow;
And bloodier yet the torrent flow
    Of Iser, rolling rapidly.

'Tis morn; but scarce yon level sun
Can pierce the war-clouds, rolling dun,
Where furious Franks and fiery Hun
    Shout in their sulphurous canopy.

The combat deepens. On, ye brave,
Who rush to glory, or the grave!
Wave, Munich, all thy banners wave,
        And charge with all thy chivalry!

Few, few shall part, where many meet!
The snow shall be their winding-sheet,
And every turf beneath their feet
        Shall be a soldier's sepulchre.

> Thomas Campbell

The Ballad of the Oysterman

It was a tall young oysterman lived by the river-side,
His shop was just upon the bank, his boat was on the tide;
The daughter of a fisherman, that was so straight and slim,
Lived over on the other bank, right opposite to him.

It was the pensive oysterman that saw a lovely maid,
Upon a moonlight evening, a-sitting in the shade!
He saw her wave her handkerchief, as much as if to say,
'I'm wide awake, young oysterman, and all the folks away.'

Then up arose the oysterman, and to himself said he,
'I guess I'll leave the skiff at home, for fear that folks should
    see;
I read it in the story-book, that, for to kiss his dear,
Leander swam the Hellespont – and I will swim this here.'

And he has leaped into the waves, and crossed the shining
    stream,
And he has clambered up the bank, all in the moonlight
    gleam;
Oh, there were kisses sweet as dew, and words as soft as
    rain, –
But they have heard her father's step, and in he leaps again!

Out spoke the ancient fisherman: 'Oh, what was that, my
    daughter?'
''Twas nothing but a pebble, sir, I threw into the water.'
'And what is that, pray tell me, love, that paddles off so
    fast?'
'It's nothing but a porpoise, sir, that's been a-swimming
    past.'

Out spoke the ancient fisherman: 'Now bring me my
   harpoon!
I'll get into my fishing-boat, and fix the fellow soon.'
Down fell that pretty innocent, as falls a snow-white lamb!
Her hair drooped round her pallid cheeks, like seaweed on
   a clam.

Alas for those two loving ones! she waked not from her
   swound,
And he was taken with the cramp, and in the waves was
   drowned!
But Fate has metamorphosed them, in pity of their woe,
And now they keep an oyster-shop for mermaids down
   below.

                    Oliver Wendell Holmes

The Griesly Wife

'Lie still, my newly married wife,
  Lie easy as you can.
You're young and ill accustomed yet
  To sleeping with a man.'

The snow lay thick, the moon was full
  And shone across the floor.
The young wife went with never a word
  Barefooted to the door.

He up and followed sure and fast,
  The moon shone clear and white.
But before his coat was on his back
  His wife was out of sight.

He trod the trail wherever it turned
  By many a mound and scree,
And still the barefoot track led on
  And an angry man was he.

He followed fast, he followed slow,
  And still he called her name,
But only the dingoes of the hills
  Yowled back at him again.

His hair stood up along his neck,
  His angry mind was gone,
For the track of the two bare feet gave out
  And a four-foot track went on.

Her nightgown lay upon the snow
    As it might upon the sheet,
But the track that led on from where it lay
    Was never of human feet.

His heart turned over in his chest,
    He looked from side to side,
And he thought more of his gumwood fire
    Than he did of his griesly bride.

At first he started walking back
    And then began to run
And his quarry wheeled at the end of her track
    And hunted him in turn.

Oh, long the fire may burn for him
    And open stand the door,
And long the bed may wait empty:
    He'll not be back any more.

John Manifold

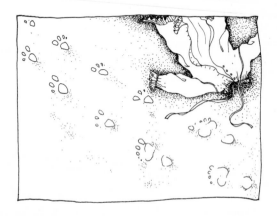

Rafferty Rides Again

There's a road outback that becomes a track
Where the hills dip down to the plain;
And on misty moonlight nights up there
The old inhabitants all declare
On his big black stallion (or was it a mare?)
Rafferty rides again.

A bushranger bold in the days of old,
'Twas an evil name that he bore,
Till they shot him down behind a tree –
At least that's the yarn they told to me
When I asked who this Rafferty bloke might be,
And what he was riding for.

And it now appears, after all the years
That low in his grave he has lain,
That o'er the hills, in the same old way,
Dashing and debonair, reckless, gay,
On his chestnut charger (or was it a bay?)
Rafferty rides again.

I have waited long the old hills among,
But my vigils have been in vain;
I've perched all night in a towering tree,
But devil a ride he'd ride for me,
Though I would have given the world to see
Rafferty ride again.

But the tale is true that I'm telling you,
Though it's ages since he was slain;
To all the folk in the hills 'tis known
That, awesome and spectral, and all alone,
On his snow-white courser (or was it roan?)
Rafferty rides again.

Thomas V. Tierney

A Girl's Song

Early one morning
As I went out walking
I saw the young sailor
Go fresh through the fields.
His eye was as blue as
The sky up above us
And clean was his skin
As the colour of shells.

O where are you going,
Young sailor, so early?
And may I come with you
A step as you go?
He looked with his eye
And I saw the deep sea-tombs,
He opened his mouth
And I heard the sea roar.

And limp on his head
Lay his hair green as sea-grass
And scrubbed were his bones
By the inching of sand.
The long tides enfolded
The lines of his body
And slow corals grow
At the stretch of his hand.

I look from my window
In the first light of morning
And I look from my door
At the dark of the day,
But all that I see are
The fields flat and empty
And the black road run down
To Cardigan town.

Leslie Norris

The Hero

'Jack fell as he'd have wished,' the Mother said,
And folded up the letter that she'd read.
'The Colonel writes so nicely.' Something broke
In the tired voice that quavered to a choke.
She half looked up. 'We mothers are so proud
Of our dead soldiers.' Then her face was bowed.

Quietly the Brother Officer went out.
He'd told the poor old dear some gallant lies
That she would nourish all her days, no doubt.
For while he coughed and mumbled, her weak eyes
Had shone with gentle triumph, brimmed with joy,
Because he'd been so brave, her glorious boy.

He thought how 'Jack', cold-footed, useless swine,
Had panicked down the trench that night the mine
Went up at Wicked Corner; how he'd tried
To get sent home, and how, at last, he died,
Blown to small bits. And no one seemed to care
Except that lonely woman with white hair.

Siegfried Sassoon

Wicked Corner part of trench system

Notting Hill Polka

We've – had –
A Body in the house
    Since father passed away:
He took bad on
Saturday night an' he
    Went the followin' day.

Mum's – pulled –
The blinds all down
    An' bought some Sherry Wine,
An' we've put the tin
What the Arsenic's in
    At the bottom of the Ser-pen-tine!

W. Bridges-Adam

Moonrise

The Barley creek was running high, the Narrows were
    abrim,
As low I crouched beside the ridge, and watched an hour
    for him.
And out against the round red moon that lipped each
    standing twig
How black the drooping gum-boughs seemed! The moon
    how bright and big!

The troopers watched the hills, I knew. But I, more wise
    than they,
Guessed that the man they hunted down would ride a nearer
    way.
If rider passed along the ridge from where I watched the
    track,
He would stand out against the moon, a silhouette in black.
So hidden in the fern I lay, for he, I loved, had sworn
That he would come to where I hid, at moonrise or at morn.
And then above the sighing wind, the leaf talk in the trees,
I thought I heard a horse's bit a-jingle in the breeze,
And all the red came to my cheeks, the kisses to my mouth,
As though a crush of roses fed the wind along the South.

I peered between the ferny cowls; I clasped my hands above
The heart that ached to cry aloud thanksgiving for its love.
I saw him black against the red. How blood-red was the
    moon!
And more of summer was the air than like a night in June,
A frosty night. And clear the sound of hoof-beats on the
    track:
And he a target on the moon, the red beyond the black.

A curlew whistled from the plain; a mopoke flapped; and
    then –
The night was full of spitting oaths, and pistol shots, and
    men.
I thought the troopers watched the hills. Ah, God, how
    could I know
Among the laces of the fern they, too, were crouching low?
I saw a trooper's grim-set face across a fallen log.
My man? Among the shattered gorse they trapped him like
    a dog!

The sergeant got his stripes for this. My man hanged
    yesterday.
... The sergeant with his new-won stripes tonight will pass
    this way.
The red moon will be full tonight, and very bright and big.
Across her face the boughs will stand, clean-cut in every
    twig;
And I shall creep among the fern – I know the old trail well,
It is the road that lies between the walls of Heaven and
    Hell –
With rifle laid across my knees I'll watch the dewy track;
The sergeant 'twixt me and the moon, a silhouette in black ...

Mabel Forrest

A Small Tragedy

They came up in the evening
And said to him, 'Fly!
All is discovered!'
And he fled.

A quiet little man,
Of no importance.
In fifty years he had acquired
Only flat feet and spectacles
And a distressing cough.

After a month or more,
(He having gone so quickly)
An inspector called
And they began to find the bodies.

A large number of them,
Stuffed into cupboards and corners.
(At work he was tidy
But files and paper-clips
Are matters of some importance.)

In the end, of course,
He was hanged,
Very neatly,
Though pleading insanity.

A quiet little man,
Who knew what to do with files and paper-clips,
But had no ideas about people
Except to destroy them.

Sally Roberts

Badger

When midnight comes a host of dogs and men
Go out and track the badger to his den,
And put a sack within the hole, and lie
Till the old grunting badger passes by.
He comes and hears – they let the strongest loose.
The old fox hears the noise and drops the goose.
The poacher shoots and hurries from the cry,
And the old hare half wounded buzzes by.
They get a forked stick to bear him down
And clap the dogs and take him to the town
And bait him all the day with many dogs,
And laugh and shout and fright the scampering hogs.
He runs along and bites at all he meets:
They shout and hollo down the noisy streets.

He turns about to face the loud uproar
And drives the rebels to their very door.
The frequent stone is hurled where'er they go;
When badgers fight, then everyone's a foe.
The dogs are clapped and urged to join the fray;
The badger turns and drives them all away.
Though scarcely half as big, demure and small,
He fights with dogs for hours and beats them all.
The heavy mastiff, savage in the fray,
Lies down and licks his feet and turns away.
The bulldog knows his match and waxes cold,
The badger grins and never leaves his hold.
He drives the crowd and follows at their heels
And bites them through – the drunkard swears and reels.

The frighted women take the boys away,
The blackguard laughs and hurries on the fray.
He tries to reach the woods, an awkward race,
But sticks and cudgels quickly stop the chase.
He turns again and drives the noisy crowd
And beats the many dogs in noises loud.
He drives away and beats them every one,
And then they loose them all and set them on.
He falls as dead and kicked by dogs and men,
Then starts and grins and drives the crowd again;
Till kicked and torn and beaten out he lies
And leaves his hold and cackles, groans, and dies.

John Clare

The Apple Raid

Darkness came early, though not yet cold;
Stars were strung on the telegraph wires;
Street lamps spilled pools of liquid gold;
The breeze was spiced with garden fires.

That smell of burnt leaves, the early dark,
Can still excite me but not as it did
So long ago when we met in the Park –
Myself, John Peters and David Kidd.

We moved out of town to the district where
The lucky and wealthy had their homes
With garages, gardens, and apples to spare
Ripely clustered in the trees' green domes.

We chose the place we meant to plunder
And climbed the wall and dropped down to
The secret dark. Apples crunched under
Our feet as we moved through the grass and dew.

The clusters on the lower boughs of the tree
Were easy to reach. We stored the fruit
In pockets and jerseys until all three
Boys were heavy with their tasty loot.

Safe on the other side of the wall
We moved back to town and munched as we went.
I wonder if David remembers at all
That little adventure, the apples' fresh scent?

Strange to think that he's fifty years old,
That tough little boy with scabs on his knees;
Stranger to think that John Peters lies cold
In an orchard in France beneath apple trees.

Vernon Scannell

Jabberwocky

'Twas brillig, and the slithy toves
Did gyre and gimble in the wabe;
All mimsy were the borogoves,
And the mome raths outgrabe.

'Beware the Jabberwock, my son!
The jaws that bite, the claws that catch!
Beware the Jubjub bird, and shun
The frumious Bandersnatch!'

He took his vorpal sword in hand:
Long time the manxome foe he sought –
So rested he by the Tumtum tree,
And stood awhile in thought.

And as in uffish thought he stood,
The Jabberwock, with eyes of flame,
Came whiffling through the tulgey wood
And burbled as it came!

One, two! One, two! And through and through
The vorpal blade went snicker-snack!
He left it dead, and with its head
He went galumphing back.

'And hast thou slain the Jabberwock?
Come to my arms, my beamish boy!
Ah frabjous day! Callooh callay!'
He chortled in his joy.

'Twas brillig, and the slithy toves
Did gyre and gimble in the wabe;
All mimsy were the borogoves,
And the mome raths outgrabe.

Lewis Carroll

Miller's End

When we moved to Miller's End,
   Every afternoon at four
A thin shadow of a shade
   Quavered through the garden-door.

Dressed in black from top to toe
   And a veil about her head
To us all it seemed as though
   She came walking from the dead.

With a basket on her arm
   Through the hedge-gap she would pass,
Never a mark that we could spy
   On the flagstones or the grass.

When we told the garden-boy
   How we saw the phantom glide,
With a grin his face was bright
   As the pool he stood beside.

'That's no ghost-walk,' Billy said,
   'Nor a ghost you fear to stop –
Only old Miss Wickerby
   On a short cut to the shop.'

So next day we lay in wait,
   Passed a civil time of day,
Said how pleased we were she came
   Daily down our garden-way.

Suddenly her cheek it paled,
    Turned, as quick, from ice to flame.
'Tell me,' said Miss Wickerby.
    'Who spoke of me, and my name?'

'Bill the garden-boy.'
                        She sighed,
    Said, 'Of course, you could not know
How he drowned – that very pool –
    A frozen winter – long ago.'

                Charles Causley

The Sands of Dee

'O Mary, go and call the cattle home,
 And call the cattle home,
 And call the cattle home
 Across the sands of Dee';
The western wind was wild and dark with foam,
 And all alone went she.

The western tide crept up along the sand,
 And o'er and o'er the sand,
 And round and round the sand,
 As far as eye could see.
The rolling mist came down and hid the land:
 And never home came she.

'O is it weed, or fish, or floating hair –
 A tress of golden hair,
 A drownèd maiden's hair,
 Above the nets at sea?'
Was never salmon yet that shone so fair
 Among the stakes of Dee.

They rowed her in across the rolling foam,
 The cruel crawling foam,
 The cruel hungry foam,
 To her grave beside the sea;
But still the boatmen hear her call the cattle home
 Across the sands of Dee.

Charles Kingsley

Death

One night as I lay on my bed,
And sleep on fleeting foot had fled,
Because, no doubt, my mind was heavy
With concern for my last journey:

I got me up and called for water,
That I might wash, and so feel better;
But before I wet my eyes so dim,
There was Death on the bowl's rim.

I went to church that I might pray,
Thinking sure he'd keep away;
But before I got on to my feet,
There sat Death upon my seat.

To my chamber then I hied,
Thinking sure he'd keep outside;
But though I firmly locked the door,
Death came from underneath the floor.

Then to sea I rowed a boat,
Thinking surely Death can't float;
But before I reached the deep,
Death was captain of my ship.

Unknown
translated from the Welsh by
Aneirin Talfan Davies

Acknowledgements

*The editors and publishers gratefully acknowledge permission to
reproduce the following copyright poems in this book:*

'A Phantasy' by John Ashbrook, reprinted by permission of
the author; 'Lady Weeping at the Crossroads' and 'O
What is That Sound' by W. H. Auden from *Collected Poems*,
reprinted by permission of Faber & Faber Ltd; 'Henry
King' by Hilaire Belloc from *Complete Verse*, reprinted by
permission of Gerald Duckworth & Co. Ltd; 'Winter:
East Anglia' by Edmund Blunden from *Poems of Many
Years* (Collins), reprinted by permission of A. D. Peters
& Co. Ltd; 'Columbus' (extract from 'The Emigrants')
by Edward Kamau Brathwaite from *Rights of Passage*,
copyright © Oxford University Press, 1967, reprinted by
permission of Oxford University Press; 'The Horse That
Had a Flat Tire' by Richard Brautigan from *The Pill
Versus the Spring Hill Mine Disaster* (Dell Publishing Co.
Inc.), reprinted by permission of Murray Pollinger;
'Friday Morning' by Sidney Carter from *Poetry and Song*
(Macmillan), edited by James Gibson, reprinted by
permission of the author; 'Miller's End' by Charles
Causley from *Collected Poems* (Macmillan), reprinted by
permission of David Higham Associates; 'The Inquest'
and 'Sleep' by W. H. Davies from *Collected Poems*, reprinted
by permission of Jonathan Cape Ltd; 'The Listeners' and
'Tom's Angel' by Walter de la Mare from *Collected Poems*
(Faber & Faber Ltd), reprinted by permission of the
Literary Trustees of Walter de la Mare and the Society
of Authors as their representative; 'Applemoon' by Rose
Flint from *Writing Poems* (Oxford University Press),
reprinted by permission of the author; 'Welsh Incident'
by Robert Graves from *Collected Poems* (Cassell), reprinted

by Vernon Scannell, reprinted by permission of the author; 'The Visitor' by Ian Serraillier from *A Second Poetry Book: An Anthology* (Oxford University Press), edited by John Foster, copyright © Ian Serraillier, 1980, reprinted by permission of the author; 'Jimmy Jet and his TV Set' by Shel Silverstein, copyright © Evil Eye Music, Inc. 1974, reprinted by permission of Harper & Row Publishers, Inc.; 'Lowery Cot' by L. A. G. Strong from *The Lowery Road* (Methuen), reprinted by permission of A. D. Peters & Co. Ltd; 'The Fugitive' by Dorothy Stuart from *Historical Songs and Ballads*, reprinted by permission of Harrap Ltd; 'Ballad' and 'Conquerors' by Henry Treece from *The Black Seasons* (Faber & Faber Ltd), reprinted by permission of John Johnson Ltd; 'A Chinese Poem written in 718 BC' from *Chinese Poems*, translated by Arthur Waley, reprinted by permission of Unwin Hyman Ltd; 'To Find a Son and Heir', 'Never Since Eden' and 'The Wily Astrologer' by Raymond Wilson, reprinted by permission of the author; 'Legend' by Judith Wright from *Judith Wright: Selected Poems, Five Senses*, reprinted by permission of Angus & Robertson Publishers; 'The Song of Wandering Aengus' by W. B. Yeats from *The Collected Poems of W. B. Yeats*, reprinted by permission of A. P. Watt Ltd on behalf of Michael B. Yeats and Macmillan London Ltd.

Index of First Lines

Index of Authors